PICSIE Books, Buckingham, England
2000

D0183361

INTRODUCTION

A MESSAGE FROM DAN JONES

There is a growing realisation that there is much more to lean than we thought. In its purest form it grows out of a genericised version of the Toyota Production System, pioneered by Taiichi Ohno and his colleagues in the early post war years. However they in turn rediscovered the path originally followed by Henry Ford in his first large plant in Highland Park. There every operation was arranged in a continuous flow sequence.

This in turn was inspired by Colt's rifle factory in Hertford back in 1855. So the idea of continuous flow has a long history.

But no one was able to follow the example of Highland Park. As soon as they needed to make a range of products they chose to organise by process, activity and department and to schedule work through each step, using ever more complicated scheduling systems. The River Rouge plant was a classic process village organisation, with big batches and long lead times. Even Henry Ford lost the plot and followed a different fork in the way! But in truth as long as markets were growing fast the hidden wastes in such a system did not matter and the error of his ways did not become apparent.

Except to Eiiji Toyoda and Taiichi Ohno - who were determined to find a way of successively overcoming all the obstacles to linking every step into a continuous flow sequence, precisely synchronised with the demand of the end customer. Twenty five years later the world woke up to the power of this alternative path - and many have been struggling to follow their example.

As they do so they discover not only the power of this alternative path, but how profoundly different it is to the traditional batch and queue path. Tools and techniques for moving from batch to flow are just the first step - the next is to combine them in the right way using the lean principles, and then to design an implementation path to transform the organisation and its relationships with its suppliers and customers down each value stream. We are at the beginning of a long journey to explore the true power of Lean.

This book will be a great help on your journey.

Best wishes

Dan Jones

The Lean Enterprise Research Centre

Europe's leading centre for Lean Management is Cardiff Business School's Lean Enterprise Research Centre. Dan Jones and Peter Hines are co-directors. The centre runs various short and long programmes including a two-year, part-time MSc in Lean Operations, with modules held at factory locations.

Telephone 029 2087 4544

Web site www.cf.ac.uk/carbs/lerc

The Lean Enterprise Institute

The Lean Enterprise Instiitute is a leading promoter of Lean Thinking. The directors are Dan Jones and Jim Womack. They stage "Lean Summit" conferences. Their web site is a must.

Web site www.lean.org

The Institute of Operations Management

The Institute of Operations Management (IOM) is the leading UK-based society for manufacturing management. They run a short course in the Lean area called "The Lean Toolbox" based on this book, and run by John Bicheno.

Telephone 02476 692266

Web site www.iomnet.org.uk

The Association for Manufacturing Excellence (AME)

In the USA, the AME is the leading non-profit society concentrating on Lean. It is strongly against the idea that "the answer" lics with systems like ERP. It pioneered the Kaizen Blitz and publishes the excellent "Target" magazine. Half or full day events are held at member companies. AME (UK) is just getting started with the same vision. Membership is a must for any organisation serious about Lean.

Contact Colin Mynott 01788 822313

E-mail: ame-uk@mynott.com

The Author

John Bicheno has graduate degrees in Engineering, Management and Systems, but more importantly, almost two decades of exposure to Lean. He is a former Associate Professor of Industrial Engineering at the University of the Witwatersrand and now directs the MSc in Lean Operations at Cardiff Business School. He also acts as "Lean Counsellor" to several organisations. He began "peeling the Lean onion" in 1984 when he worked with Toyota, GEC and Afrox in South Africa. He is still peeling.

CONTENTS

PAGE

THE ROAD TO AWAY FROM LEAN   8-11

PHILOSOPHY   12

Lean Thinking   12
15 Characteristics of Lean   14
Agile Operations   15
The Elements of Agility   18
Time Based Competition   19
Muda   21
The Sustainable Lean Enterprise and the R's of Lean   27
Gemba   28

PLANNING   30

Scenarios   30
Time Pacing   32
Value Focused Thinking   33
Policy Deployment and Cross Functional Management   34
Target Costing   38

DESIGN AND NEW PRODUCTS   41

Development Time and Organising for New Products   41
Four Objectives and Six Trade-offs   44
Simultaneous and Concurrent Engineering   45
Mass Customisation and Modularity   48
Design for Manufacture   50
Product Platforms   52
Four Fields Mapping   55
Quality Function Deployment   57
TRIZ   63
Concept Screening   65

ANALYSIS AND MAPPING   67

Takt Time   67
System Dynamics, Systems Thinking, and Learning   68
Product Contribution Analysis   73
The Muda Map   74
Storyboarding and Brown Paper Exercise   75
Value Stream Mapping   78
    Overall Lead Time Mapping   78
    Order Mapping   80
    Customer Mapping   82
    "Learning to See" Mapping   83

	PAGE
Process Activity Mapping	85
Product Variety Funnel	89
Quality Filter Mapping	90
Demand Amplification Mapping	90
Push Pull Mapping	93
Physical Structure Mapping	94
Capacity Mapping	94
Cost Time Profile	96
Business Process Mapping	98
Time Charting and Analysis	100
Soft Systems Methodology	102
Self Audits	105

IMPROVEMENT — 110

Continual Improvement	110
5S	113
Kaikaku	115
Standards	118
String Diagrams	120
Value Engineering and Value Analysis	120
Kaizen	124
Total Productive Maintenance (TPM)	126
Overall Equipment Effectiveness (OEE)	129
Root Cause Analysis	130
Business Process Reengineering (BPR)	132

PRODUCTION — 135

Little's Law	135
Kanban	136
Batch Sizing	144
Changeover Reduction	148
Mixed Model Production	149
Runners, Repeaters, Strangers	150
Demand Smoothing (Heijunka)	150
Group Technology and Cellular Manufacturing	153
Inventory Issues: Cost, Waste, Safety Stocks	158
Visual and Audio Management	159
Point of Production Control	162

GOLDRATT — 163

Throughput, inventory, operating expense	163
Dependent events, statistical fluctuation	163
Constraints, bottlenecks and the synchronous rules	164
Drum, buffer, rope	165
Theory of constraints and thinking process	166

	PAGE
QUALITY	170
The Kano Model	170
Failsafing (Pokayoke)	172
Short Run SPC	174
Precontrol	176
SUPPLIERS AND **D**ISTRIBUTION	178
Supplier Partnerships	178
Supplier Associations	181
Integrated Supply	183
PEOPLE	184
Open Book Management	184
Meetings, Memos and Responsibilities	186
Change Management	187
Ubuntu and Kyosei	188
MEASUREMENT	190
Management Accounting and Activity Based Costing	190
Kaizen Costing and Pseudo Profit Centres	193
Performance Measurement and the Balanced Scorecard	195
Productivity Accounting	200

THE ROAD TO (AND AWAY FROM) LEAN

SIGNIFICANT DATES

1893 F.W. Taylor begins work as a "consulting engineer"

1896 Vilfredo Pareto publishes law of economic distribution

1898 F.W. Taylor begins his time studies of shovelling of iron

1904 Cadillac begins building cars using interchangeable parts

1908 Ford Model T

1909 Frank and Lillian Gilbreth study bricklaying. Beginnings of motion study.

1911 F.W. Taylor "Principles of Scientific Management"

1913 Ford establishes Highland Park plant using the moving assembly line. First lean?

1915 Wilson EOQ formula

1922 Gantt "The Gantt Chart: A Working Tool for Management"

1925 "Mass Production" phrase coined by Encyclopaedia Britannica

1926 Henry Ford "Today and Tomorrow"

1927 Establishment of Toyota Motor (Toyota looms established in 1922)

1927-1930 Mayo and Roethlisberger studies at Hawthorn Plant of Western Electric

1931 Walter Shewhart. "Economic Control of Quality of Manufactured Product" Van Nostrand. First book on SPC

1934 H.B. Maynard coins the term "Method Study"

1936 An engineer at General Motors coins the term "automation"

1942 Juran: Reengineering procurement for Lend Lease (90 days to 53 hours)

1943-1944 Flow production of bombers at Boeing Plant II and Ford Willow Run

1945 Shigeo Shingo presents concept of production as a network to JMA. Also identifies batch production as the main source of delays

1948 Deming first sent to Japan.
Lectures on waste as being the prime source of quality problems

1949 Juran first goes to Japan

1950 Eiji Toyoda visits Ford's River Rouge plant

1950 Ohno begins work on the Toyota Production System following strikes

1951 Deming Award established in Japan

1951 Juran "Handbook of Quality Control" (first edition). Includes cost of quality, Pareto analysis, SPC. (Fifth edition published 1999)

1961 Jay Forrester, "Industrial Dynamics", MIT Press, describes supply chain system dynamics and demand amplification.

1961 Shigeo Shingo devises and defines "pokayoke", book published in 1985

1961 Ishikawa devises Quality Circles, and first are set up in 1962. Juran introduces the concept in Europe in 1966.

1961 Feigenbaum, "Total Quality Control", McGraw Hill

1969 First microchip designed at Intel by Ted Hoff

1971 Mudge, "Value Engineering: A Systematic Approach", McGraw Hill

1971 WalMart begins point of sale. Forerunner of EDI, Quick Response, FMCG

1974 Wickham Skinner "The Focused Factory" HBR

1975 Shingo explains "non stock production system"

1975 Orlicky, "Material Requirements Planning", McGraw Hill

1975 Burbidge, "The Introduction of Group Technology", Heinemann

1977 Apple, "Plant Layout and Materials Handling", Wiley

1978 APICS MRP Crusade

1979 First articles on "Just in Time" appear in US magazines.

1980 NBC television screens "If Japan Can, Why can't We?"

1982 Deming "Quality, Productivity and Competitive Position" MIT Press

1982 Deming "Out of the Crisis" MIT Press. Contains his 14 point plan.

1982 Schonberger "Japanese Manufacturing Techniques", Free Press

1983 Hall, "Zero Inventories", Dow Jones Irwin APICS

1983 Monden, "Toyota Production System", Ind Eng and Management Press

1984 Eli Goldratt "The Goal"

1984 Hayes and Wheelwright, "Restoring our Competitive Edge", Free Press

1984 Kaplan "Yesterday's Accounting Undermines Production" HBR and 1987 Kaplan & Johnson "Relevance Lost: The Rise and Fall of Management Accounting"

1985 Shingo: "SMED", Productivity

1985 Skinner, "Manufacturing: The Formidable Competitive Weapon", Wiley

1985 NUMMI (GM/Toyota joint venture) produces fiirst vehicle. Becomes highest-ranking plant in GM for quality in 1986. GM invested $60billion in technology 1982-1985

1985 Hill, "Manufacturing Strategy", Macmillan

1985 Porter, "Competitive Advantage", Free Press - proposes Value Chains

1986 Maasaki Imai "Kaizen – The Key to Japan's Competitive Success"

1986 Nissan's UK plant established at Sunderland. In 1999 it remains the most productive car plant in Europe with 105 vehicles per man per year.

1986 Goldratt and Fox "The Race"

1987 Baldridge award established

1987 Amercan Apparel Manufactures "Getting Started in Quick Response"

1987 Boothroyd and Dewhurst "Design for Assembly"

1988 Nakajima "Introduction to Total Productive Maintenance"

1988 Ohno "The Toyota Production System", Productivity Press

1988 Akao introduces QFD into manufacturing

1988 Cooper and Kaplan, "Measure Costs Right: Make the Right Decision", HBR (First paper on ABC)

1989 Camp "Benchmarking: The Search for Industry Best Practices", ASQ Quality Press

1990 Stalk and Hout: "Competing against Time", Free Press

1990 Hammer "Reengineering Work: Don't automate, Obliterate" HBR, and
1994 Hammer and Champy "Reengineering the Corporation"

1990 Stuart Pugh "Total Design", and 1981 Concept Selection

1990 Womack and Jones "The Machine that Changed the World", Rawson

1990 Schonberger, "Building a Chain of Customers", Free Press

1990 GM's Saturn plant begins production. Later to be top of JD Powers for four successive years. GM makes a loss of $2 billion.

1990 Osborn, Moran, Musselwhite, Zenger, "Self Directed Work Teams", Business One

1992 Jack Stack, "The Great Game of Business", Currency Doubleday, sets out Open Book management.

1992 EFQM award established

1993 WWW established. Internet expands from military and university area.

1993 Joseph Pine, "Mass Customisation", Harvard

1993 AME popularises "Kaizen Blitz"

1994 Altshuller, First English translation of book about TRIZ

1996 Womack and Jones "Lean Thinking", Simon and Schuster

1996 Hopp and Spearman, "Factory Physics", Irwin

1998 Rajan Suri "Quick Response Manufacturing", Productivity Press

1999 Gates: "Business at the Speed of Thought" proposes "The Digital Nervous System"

2000 Ford begins Amazon plant. An attempt to bring back the ideals of Highland Park

Note: HBR denotes Harvard Business Review

PHILOSOPHY

➡ Lean Thinking
➡ 14 Characteristics of Lean
➡ Agile Operations
➡ The Elements of Agility
➡ Time Based Competition
➡ Muda
➡ The Sustainable Lean Enterprise and the R's of Lean
➡ Gemba

LEAN THINKING

In their book *The Machine That Changed The World*, Womack, Jones and Roos not only renewed the JIT message that had been around for a decade in the West, but also brought home, in elegant prose, the message that Western manufacturing was slipping still further behind. The book centred on the car industry, and delivered a stinging rebuff to those in the industry who were saying "we already have that in place". Six years later, in *Lean Thinking*, Womack and Jones once again renewed the message, but extended it out beyond the car industry. These reflective authors have given manufacturing, but to an extent also service, a vision of a world transformed from mass production to lean enterprise. The five principles set forth are of fundamental importance. Reading the Introduction to *Lean Thinking* should be compulsory for every executive; unfortunately the past two decades have shown that the message is likely to lead to real change in only a few cases.

A central theme of Lean Thinking is the elimination of Muda (or waste). Womack and Jones have given some powerful examples of just how much of it there is still around, despite two decades of JIT and ten years of reengineering. One example concerns the production of aluminium cola cans from Bauxite to Tesco supermarket shelf. This takes 319 days, during which time value is being added for only 3 hours. Keep in mind that there are sophisticated "world class" companies along this route.

Taiichi Ohno's 7 muda or wastes are given a separate section in this book. Womack and Jones point out that there are three types of activity: value creating, non-value creating but unavoidable with present technologies or methods, and pure waste. This is the basis of the value mapping tools described in later sections. But note that waste may not be identified as waste unless the complete value stream is looked at. An example is an operator diligently adding a feature that is removed at another company further along the stream.

THE FIVE LEAN PRINCIPLES

In this section, whilst using Womack and Jones' 5 principles, some liberties have been taken. Some managers are upset by the five principles, believing them not to be feasible within their industry. But this is to miss the point, which is vision: you may not get there within your lifetime, but try - others certainly will.

The starting point is to specify value from the point of view of the customer. This is an established marketing idea (that customers buy results, not products - a clean shirt, not a washing machine). Too often, however, manufacturers tend to give the customers what is convenient for the manufacturer, or deemed economic for the customer. Womack and Jones cite batch-and-queue airline travel, involving long trips to the airport to enable big batch flights which start where you ain't and take you where you don't wanna go, via hubs, and numerous delays much like the aluminium cola can. How often are new product designs undertaken constrained by existing manufacturing facilities rather than by customer requirements? Of course we have to know who is the customer: the final customer, or the next process, or the next company along the chain, or the customer's customer.

Then identify the value stream. This is the sequence of processes all the way from raw material to final customer, or from product concept to market launch. If possible look at the whole supply chain (or probably more accurately the "demand network"). Again, an established idea from TQM / Juran / business processing. You are only as good as the weakest link; supply chains compete, not companies. Think of the three types of action (above), and eliminate the wastes. The value stream should be mapped, and a whole section of this book is devoted to this topic. In mapping, focus horizontally on the item, not vertically on the departmental silo. Track the experiences of the product or customer, not the experiences of the manager or operator. Focus horizontally, not vertically.

The third principle is Flow. Make value flow. If possible use one piece flow. Keep it moving. Avoid batch and queue, or at least continuously reduce them and the obstacles in their way. Try to design according to Stalk and Hout's Golden Rule - never to delay a value adding step by a non value adding (although temporarily necessary) step - try to do such steps in parallel. Flow requires much JIT preparation activity. This includes modular design, product platforms, cells, small machines, changeover reduction, multiskilled operators, supplier partnership, and enablers such as 5S, TPM, and TQ. But the important thing is vision: you have to have in mind a guiding strategy that will move you inexorably towards flow.

Then comes Pull. Having set up the framework for flow, only make as needed. Pull according to customer demand. Pull reduces time and waste. Do not overproduce. Of course, pull needs to take place along the whole demand flow network, not only within a company. So this ultimately implies sharing final customer demands right along the chain. Now of course, in some industries true pull, instant response is not possible - you cannot grow an orange tree overnight to provide a pulled orange drink - but you can pull for several stages back from the customer, and each extension of pull reduces forecast uncertainty.

Finally comes Perfection. Having worked through the previous principles, suddenly now "perfection" seems more possible. Perfection does not mean only quality - it means producing exactly what the customer wants, exactly when (with no delay), at a fair price and with minimum waste. Beware of benchmarking - the real benchmark is zero waste, not what the competitors are doing.

One quickly realises that these five principles are not a sequential, one off procedure, but rather a journey of continuous improvement. Start out today.

FURTHER READING:
James Womack and Daniel Jones, *Lean Thinking,* Simon and Schuster, New York, 1996, ISBN 0-684-81035-2

THE 15 CHARACTERISTICS OF LEAN

The literature on JIT and Lean contains several seminal books, amongst them by Womack and Jones, Schonberger, Hall, Goldratt, and Imai. These built on the "greats": Deming, Juran, and Ohno. To distil them is a daunting task, but certainly there are common themes. These 15 seem to be at the core:

→ **CUSTOMER** – The external customer is the starting and ending point. Seek to maximise value to the customer. Optimise around the customer, not around internal operations. Understand the customer's true demand, what he would really like, not what can be supplied.

→ **SIMPLICITY** – Lean is not simple, but simplicity pervades. Simplicity in operation, in system, in technology, in control is the goal. Simplicity applies to product through part count reduction and commonality. Simplicity applies to suppliers through working closely with a few trusted partners. Simplicity applies in the plant, by creating focused factories-within-a -factory. Beware complex computer systems, complex and large automation, complex product lines, complex rewards. Select the smallest, most simple machine possible consistent with quality requirements.

→ **VISIBILITY** – Seek to make all operations as visible and transparent as possible. Control by sight. Adopt the visual factory.

→ **REGULARITY** – Regularity makes for "no surprises" operations. We run our lives on regularity (sleep, breakfast, etc); we should run our operations on this basis too. Seek "repeater" products and run them in the same time slots - this cuts inventory, improves quality, and allows simplicity of control. "Time pacing" in new product introduction shortens the development cycle and makes innovation the norm.

→ **SYNCHRONISATION** – Seek "keep it moving" manufacture. Seek flow, especially one-piece flow. Synchronise operations so that the streams meet just in time.

→ **PULL** – Seek for operations to work at the customer's rate of demand. Avoid overproduction. Have pull-based demand chains, not push-based supply chains. Pull should take place at the customer's rate of demand. In demand chains this should be the final customer, not distorted by intermediate "bullwhip" effects.

→ **WASTE** – Waste is endemic. Learn to recognise it, and seek to reduce it, always. Everyone from chairman to cleaner should wear "muda spectacles" at all times.

→ **PROCESS** – Organise and think by the process view, the supply chain perspective. Think horizontal, not vertical. Concentrate on the way the product moves, not on the way the machines or people or services move. Map to understand the process.

→ **PREVENTION** – Seek to prevent problems, rather than to inspect and fix. Shift the emphasis from failure and appraisal to prevention. Inspecting the process, not the product, is prevention.

→ **TIME** – Seek to reduce overall time to make, to deliver, and to introduce new products. Use simultaneous, parallel, and overlapping operations in operations, design, and support services. Seek never to delay a value-adding step by a non value-adding step. Time is the best single overall measure.

→ **IMPROVEMENT** – Improvement, and continuous improvement in particular, is everyone's concern. Make improvement both "enforced" and passive, both incremental and breakthrough. Improvement goes beyond waste reduction to include innovation.

→ **PARTNERSHIP** – Seek co-operative working both internally between functions, and externally with suppliers. Supply chains compete, not companies. Employees are partners too. Seek to build trust.

→ **GEMBA** – Go the workplace and seek the facts. Manage by walking around. Implementation takes place on the floor, not in the office. Encourage the spirit of Gemba throughout.

→ **VARIATION** – Variation is found in every process. Seek to reduce it. Measure it, know the limits, and learn to distinguish between natural variation and special events. Manage it. Build in appropriate flexibility. Shockproof the system.

→ **PARTICIPATION** – Give operators the first opportunity to solve problems. All employees should share responsibility for success and for failure. True participation implies full information sharing.

AGILE OPERATIONS

Lean has been called Lean because it uses less of everything; less space, less inventory, less people, less time. Womack and Jones showed this elegantly in their books. But the world of operations is never static. A new dawn in operations has broken:

→ Cusumano and Nobeoka show that the Japanese are now taking longer, using more project managers, and more common parts in 1990 than they were in 1980. Possibly more emphasis is being placed on cost, variety and service rather than on time.

→ The use of platforms and modularity is growing in all industries. They look like becoming fundamental building blocks, allowing not only greater product variety and flexibility but also a redefined role for suppliers.

→ Waste reduction is still central, but the concept of waste has widened to include the product lifecycle and resource conservation. (See the section on the 5 R's.) Toyota, in a recent supplement in Time magazine said that a car, like a cat, should have nine lives with materials being re-used.

→ Benetton manufactures in a network of electronically linked partners.

→ VW uses limited assembly outsourcing at its Brazilian plant.

→ Ford is moving towards outsourcing final assembly, and the company appears to see itself as a maker of global consumer products and supplier of services rather than a car manufacturer. One assembly contractor comes from within the Fiat group, a direct competitor. Ford will focus on design, branding, marketing and service.

→ Daimler-Chrysler uses an in-house out-sourced system of manufacture for its Smart car. Several suppliers have facilities on site.

→ The use of "JIT-II" type supplier concepts has grown rapidly since its inception at Bose in 1990.

→ The huge rise is remanufacturing has been one of the quiet revolutions of the 1990s, a trend which is certain to accelerate. "Reman" often demands extreme flexibility, and whole new approaches to bills of materials and material control. At the time of writing, no general operations management textbook is known which deals with this significant trend.

→ Use of intranets and the internet. For instance, GM Saturn plant's use of a Windows NT-based intranet for monitoring 120,000 control points, and Honda's 24-hour per day world-distributed design process.

There is a great deal of confusion over the term "Agile". Kidd makes the useful statement that Lean Operations are necessary but not sufficient for Agile Manufacturing. Ansari however says that "Lean Production is a broad concept and encompasses terms such as flexible manufacturing, mass customisation, and even agile manufacturing". A supreme example of Agility built on Lean was shown in the case of the Aisin fire. This single-source Toyota supplier of P-valves suffered a catastrophic fire in February 1997. Within days, the network of Toyota suppliers, many of which had no experience in manufacturing these products, were sending parts to Aisin for inspection prior to shipment to Toyota. The problem-solving mentality and spirit of partnership fostered by Toyota were probably the main reasons why only a few days assembly line production was lost. Other reasons were the breadth and depth of engineering skills, the willingness to solve the problem first and sort out compensation later and the existence of a supplier association. If anything, the experience reinforced the commitment to JIT and Lean.

Some Agile Manufacturers claim that their aims are different from Lean Manufacturers, but it is difficult to see how. For instance, the "Japanese Manufacturing Twenty First Century Consortium" put forward nine challenges that Agile car manufacturers must address. These are (1) to break dependency on economies of scale - for example through setup reduction, (2) to produce vehicles in low volumes, economically, for example by using product platforms, (3) to aim for a "three day" car (that is the time from placing an order to receiving it to your specification), (4) to have many small assembly plants located close to customers, rather than mega plants, (5) to aim for maximum use of common components, (6) to make work interesting and challenging for operators, (7) to involve the customer in product design, or at least in product specification, (8) to establish supplier partnerships, (9) to analyse data quickly and accurately. To the author, these aims overlap significantly with lean manufacturing.

So what is "Agile"? A quick view is that Flexibility has been added to the Cost, Quality and Delivery objectives of Lean. $A = (C+Q+D)+F$. Probably a fair description is that it extends Lean Operations with the best in computer networking, the best in creative teamworking, the best in appropriate automation, the best in environmentally-conscious operations and the best in customer service. An example would be the US grocery firm Webvan which operates Internet ordering but for 50k items against the typical 30k offered in a US supermarket, and free delivery for orders over $50. It achieves this by through impressive Internet technology, but also by detailed attention to waste in facility costs, order picking and logistics. Order pickers move a maximum of 6.5m, tote bags are a careful compromise, local transfer stations are used and delivery routes optimised. Building costs and inventories are sharply down. From total energy and space perspectives there are huge savings over conventional supermarkets.

From a wider perspective, "Agility" involves bringing together core skills and competencies from several organisations in order to achieve convenience, flexibility, cost and service. An agile partnership may be for a short or longer period, and will involve partners who often regard each other as equals irrespective of differences in size. The important thing is that each partner brings certain unique core skills to the party.

An Agile manufacturer may be a "virtual" organisation (like virtual computer memory) which may not exist physically as one unit, but appears to customers as a single unit. An agile manufacturer may be dominated by a single organisation (referred to as a "prime web") or not (referred to as a "democratic web"). In a prime web, the largest company may not be the prime site - what counts is the core product.

Benetton is an agile manufacturer of the prime web type, which co-operates with many designers and manufacturers in Italy, and with many shops throughout the world, most of which use the name but are privately owned. Benetton itself also contributes design and manufacturing competence but leverages itself with computer technology. In another case, Ross Operating Valves of Georgia USA uses its own CAD software capability to design valves on a customer's site, and then download to its own manufacturing facilities or those of a third party which may be better placed geographically. Mass customisation principles are applicable in both these cases. See the separate section.

Agility has been boosted in recent years by advances in computer and telecommunications technology. An example is the Boeing 777 which used common CAD software amongst all participating companies, enabling each to keep abreast with all others, and allowing simulated "walk through" of the aircraft as it developed. In the case of the 777, even companies that were competitors on other projects shared the same software. Geographical location was of no concern. Moreover, the software will allow the partners to cooperate in the thousands of modifications that are expected during the life of the aircraft.

With the extension of Internet use, the possibilities for establishing and running agile manufacturing improves every day. Small companies and even individuals are already members of agile or virtual manufacturing companies. Thus an agile or virtual manufacturer may be able to, simultaneously, achieve fast time to market, at low cost, whilst minimising risk, and gaining access to markets beyond the scope of most of the partners taken individually.

Some agile manufacturers may be latent partnerships, lying in wait for new project opportunities to which they can respond instantly with ready-to-go people and facilities, which most single organisations would find hard to match. Other agile manufacturers may comprise companies that compete in one part of the world but cooperate in another part of the world.

A requirement for an agile manufacturer comprising several partners is that all have compatible equipment and software. This makes it possible for (say) a design house to download to suppliers and assemblers who in turn should synchronise their schedules electronically. For this to succeed, members of a virtual or agile grouping should prequalify. Many of the activities described in the Supplier Partnership section of this book are relevant. The U.S. government CALS (computer aided logistics system) has established standards for documentation which are beginning to be adopted worldwide. Some other organisations having similar objectives are given below.

FURTHER READING:

Joseph C. Montgomery and Lawrence Levine (eds), *The Transition to Agile Manufacturing,* ASQC Quality Press, Milwaukee, 1996. ISBN 0-87389-347-6

Steven Goldman, Roger Nagel, Kenneth Preiss, *Agile Competitors and Virtual Organisations,* van Nostrand Rienhold, New York, 1995. ISBN 0-442-01903-3

Michael Cusumano and Kentaro Nobeoka, *Thinking Beyond Lean,* The Free Press, New York, 1998, ISBN 0-684-84918-6

Toshihiro Nishiguchi and Alexandre Beaudet, The Toyota Group and the Aisin Fire, *Sloan Management Review,* Fall 1998, pp49-59

Agility is promoted by
The Iacocca Institute, Lehigh University, Bethlehem, PA
The Agile Manufacturing Forum
Franhofer Institute (IPIC), Berlin, Germany
The Association for Manufacturing Excellence (AME), Portland, OR.
APICS has a Remanufacturing Special Interest Group.

THE ELEMENTS OF AGILITY

If Lean establishes the foundation for Agile Manufacturing, what are the additional factors that extend traditional Lean to become more Agile? We may represent this as a fishbone diagram. See the figure.

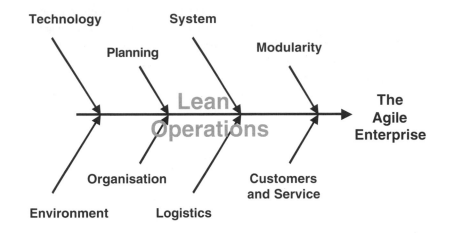

The central spine of the fish is Lean Operations itself. This is the backbone, without which there can be no Agility. The "enablers" for Agility are the bones. These are:

TECHNOLOGY – These are the technologies of flexible manufacturing. Robots, CAD, NC/CNC. They include small footprint machines with services at the back. They are not the seemingly flexible (but actually wasteful, inflexible) large automated transfer lines, large machining centres, FMS, and the AS/RS (except possibly in distribution).

PLANNING – Flexible planning tools including finite scheduling when used for planning, but not for execution. Not MRPII used for control, although MPS would often be used and MRP sometimes used for planning where appropriate. ERP, but only using the minimum necessary modules, and then only for planning. And only after much simplification and waste reduction. Specialist simulation tools used for planning and "what if".

SYSTEM – The use of networking, the Internet, and appropriate e commerce. Especially to link a network of suppliers, and to transfer designs and specifications electronically. To enter customer orders and specifications. The ability to learn about customer requirements quickly. Configurators. Computers to speed response times and improve service. Used horizontally rather than in vertical silos.

MODULARITY – The supreme way of achieving flexibility, as well as cost, quality and delivery. It is the enabling principle for networks of suppliers to use their own expertise and combining it with that of others for mutual advantage. Already well established in computer and car design, new forms are beginning to appear. In VW's Brazilian truck plant suppliers use their own workforce on VW's assembly line to build the vehicle. Subcontracting of computer services is not unusual. Fidelity Investments use an outside firm to run one of its funds.

ORGANISATION – In company and inter-company. In company including streamlined, process oriented organisation structures and HR policies that encourage innovation, improvement and participation. What Sasser calls the "Service Profit Chain" with employee capability, employee satisfaction, employee loyalty, leading to employee productivity, leading to customer satisfaction and customer loyalty, feeding back to further employee capability, satisfaction, and loyalty. Inter-company organisation including building partnership and trust along the supply chain. This also includes the use of appropriate, parsimonious control and measurement systems. The measures and controls must encourage, not discourage Lean. Open Book management.

CUSTOMERS AND SERVICE – Although Womack and Jones' first principle is to begin with the customer, agility means flexibility in product offerings and design up to and beyond the point of delivery. "Mass customisation" as well as "Quick Response" will become the norm. This goes beyond the 4 P's of marketing to include the product-service bundle, and to work towards customer retention, referrals, and repeat business. Managing all customer "moments of truth".

ENVIRONMENT – Managing processes in an environmentally responsible yet profitable way. Concerned with Redesign for life cycles, Reducing materials and energy, Recovering materials and energy during manufacture and use, Recycling after product use, and Remanufacturing.

LOGISTICS – Running the supply or demand chain for agility. This includes the technology of agile logistics (cross-docking, small unit distribution), the "software" (quick response systems, EDI, EPOS), and selecting and tailoring appropriate channels to focused customer groupings (like Coke's multi channel distribution system each tailored for a specific customer requirement, rather than for overall cost reduction).

TIME BASED COMPETITION

Stalk and Hout's classic work, *Competing Against Time,* was one of the first to identify the importance of time to the competitive edge. In the book, Stalk and Hout set out four "rules of response" which are provocative rules of thumb, but apparently based on research by the Boston Consulting Group.

→ The 0.05 to 5 rule, states that, across many industries, value is actually being added for between 0.05% and 5% of total time. (This is no longer a surprise, see for instance the earlier section on Lean Thinking).

→ The 3/3 rule, states that the wait time, during which no value is added, is split 3 ways, each accounting for approximately one third of time. The three ways are waiting for completion of batches, waiting for "physical and intellectual rework", and waiting for management decisions to send the batch forward.

→ The 1/4-2-20 rule, which states that for every quartering of total completion time, there will be a doubling of productivity and a 20% cost reduction.

→ The 3 x 2 rule, states that time based competitors enjoy growth rates of three times the average, and twice the profit margin, for their industry.

Cooper has pointed out the three major payoffs to bringing products to market faster:

→ Speed yields competitive advantage through being first to market – provided it is not an ill-conceived product.

→ Speed yields higher profitability because revenue is realised earlier, and discounted cash flow teaches that money today is worth more than money tomorrow. Getting on the learning curve earlier means cost advantages.

→ Speed means fewer surprises, since the time for market conditions and for customer preferences to change is reduced

Note that there may be good reasons for emphasising speed or reduction in lead-time even though customers may not be interested in reduced lead times.

Becoming a time-based competitor is really what this book is all about. Like Womack and Jones, Stalk and Hout recommend process mapping. They talk about the "Golden Rule of Time Based Competitiveness" which is never to delay a customer value adding step by a non-value adding step. Instead, seek to do such steps in parallel.

FURTHER READING:
George Stalk and Thomas Hout, *Competing Against Time,* The Free Press, New York, 1990, ISBN 0-02-915291-7
Robert Cooper, *Winning at New Products: Accelerating the Process from Idea to Launch,* (Second ed.), Perseus Books, Reading, MA, 1993

MUDA

Muda" is Japanese for waste. But in manufacturing, and increasingly in service, "muda" is a more powerful word than waste because it has come to be associated with the set of 7 wastes, with kaizen, with Gemba, and with JIT or "world class" in general.

Taiichi Ohno, father of the Toyota Production System, of JIT, and patriarch of Lean Operations, originally assembled the 7 wastes, but it was Deming who emphasised waste reduction in Japan in the 1950's. Today, however, it is appropriate to add to Ohno's famous list, presumptuous though that may be. The section which follows begins with Ohno's original seven, then adds seven "new" wastes.

Waste is the opposite of value. So as another dimension to the waste categories, one can think of different types of waste:

➔ Process waste (for instance changeover time, SPC, planning, evaluation, etc) which are currently necessary for the process, but do not add to customer value. Such activities are temporarily necessary waste. Aim to reduce then eliminate.

➔ Business waste (for instance, it benefits managers, employees, suppliers). These too are waste, and need to be critically examined for efficiency or elimination.

➔ Pure waste, which should be eliminated as soon as possible.

THE WASTE OF OVERPRODUCTION

Ohno believed that the waste of overproduction was the most serious of all the wastes because it was the root of so many problems. Overproduction is making too much, too early or "just-in-case". The aim should be to make exactly what is required, no more and no less, just in time and with perfect quality. Overproduction discourages a smooth flow of goods or services. "Lumpiness" (i.e. making products or working in erratic bursts) is a force against quality and productivity. By contrast, regularity encourages a "no surprises" atmosphere which may not be very exciting but is much better management.

Overproduction leads directly to excessive lead time and storage times. As a result defects may not be detected early, products may deteriorate, and artificial pressures on work rate may be generated. All these increase the chances of defects. Taking it further, overproduction leads to excessive work-in-process inventories that lead to the physical separation of operations and the discouragement of communication.

Yet overproduction is often the natural state. People do not have to be encouraged to overproduce; they often do so "just to be safe". Often this is reinforced by a bonus system that encourages output that is not needed. By contrast, the Kanban system prevents unplanned overproduction by allowing work to move forwards only when the next work area is ready to receive it. Although kanban was made famous in manufacturing, it was originally developed from the supermarket restocking procedure and certainly has application in the service industry. (Hamburgers are only made at a rate in line with demand and clerical operations are most effective when there is a uniform flow of work.) The motto "sell daily? make daily!" is as relevant in an office as it is in a factory.

Overproduction should be related to a particular timeframe. At Toyota, overproduction is considered to have occurred if the daily schedule is exceeded. Most other companies should consider a week as the no-overproduction target.

Quality guru Joseph Juran noted that in Japan in the 1950s there were severe disruptions in power supplies, with production sometimes possible for only 3 hours per day. In such circumstances making the wrong product, or making it too early, or working on an already defective item was something to be strongly avoided. Likewise the transport infrastructure was awful. Transporting the wrong item, too early, or if defective was also a huge waste. It was in these circumstances that Taiichi Ohno developed the JIT system, and led him to conclude that overproduction is the worst sin of all.

Examples: "lumpy" flow, production above target, excessive lead-time, and delivery too early.

THE WASTE OF WAITING

The waste of waiting occurs whenever time is not being used effectively. Time is an important element of competitiveness and quality. Customers do not appreciate being kept waiting but they may be prepared to pay a premium to be dealt with faster.

In a factory, any time that materials or components are seen to be not moving (or not having value added) is an indication of waste. Waiting is the enemy of smooth flow. Although it may be very difficult to reduce waiting to zero, the goal remains. Whether the waiting is of parts in a factory or customers in a bank there should always be an awareness of a non-ideal situation and a questioning of how the situation can be improved.

When operators and employees are waiting for work or simply waiting for something to do, it is waste. Can the time not be better spent on another operation or on training, cleaning, maintaining, checking, practising changeovers or even deliberate relaxation? All of these are forces for improved quality and productivity. But they require management to have developed a contingency plan on the best use of time.

A bottleneck operation that is waiting for work is a waste. As Goldratt has pointed out in his book "The Goal", "an hour lost at a bottleneck is an hour lost for the whole plant". Effective use of bottleneck time is a key to regular production that in turn strongly influences productivity and quality. (See Section on Goldratt).

Examples: operators waiting, operators slower than line, operators watching machines, late delivery, queuing at a toolcrib.

THE WASTE OF TRANSPORTING

Customers do not pay to have goods moved around (unless they have hired a removal service!). So any movement of materials in a factory is waste. It is a waste that can never be fully eliminated but it is also a waste that over time should be continually reduced. The number of transport and material handling operations is directly proportional to the likelihood of damage and deterioration. Double handling is a waste that affects productivity and quality.

Transporting is closely linked to communication. Where distances are long, communication is discouraged and quality may be the victim. Feedback on poor quality is inversely related to transportation length, whether in manufacturing or in services. There is increasingly the awareness that for improved quality in manufacturing or services, people from interacting groups need to be located physically closer together. For instance, the design office may be placed deliberately near the production area.

When this waste gains recognition by employees steps can be taken to reduce it. Measures include monitoring the flow lengths of products through a factory or paper through an office. The number of steps, and in particular the number of non-value adding steps, should be monitored. See the Section on Mapping.

Many conveyors represent poor practice because they "freeze in" the waste of transporting. And small-wheeled containers, moved by hand or in a train should replace forklifts.

Examples: double handling, all movements by forklift, conveyors

THE WASTE OF INAPPROPRIATE PROCESSING

Inappropriate processing refers to the waste of "using a hammer to crack a nut". Thinking in terms of one big machine instead of several smaller ones discourages operator "ownership", leads to pressure to run the machine as often as possible rather than only when needed, and encourages general purpose machines that may not be ideal for the need at hand. It also leads to poor layout, which as we have seen in the previous section, leads to extra transportation and poor communication. So the ideal is to use the smallest machine, capable of producing the required quality, distributed to the points of use.

Inappropriate processing also refers to machines and processes that are not quality capable. In other words, a process that cannot help but make defects. In general, a capable process requires having the correct methods, training, and tools, as well as having the required standards, clearly known. The ideal is to have machines with available capacity exactly matched to demand.

Note that it is important to take the longer-term view. Buying that large machining centre may just jeopardise the possibility of cells for many years to come. Think "small is beautiful". Smaller machines avoid bottlenecks, improve flow lengths, perhaps are more simple, can be maintained at different times (instead of affecting the whole plant), and may improve cashflow and keep up with technology (buying one small machine per year, instead of one big machine every five years).

Examples: variation between operators, variation from standard, having to use a "fast" machine shared between several lines.

THE WASTE OF UNNECESSARY INVENTORY

Although having no inventory is a goal that can never be attained, inventory is the enemy of quality and productivity. This is so because inventory tends to increase leadtime, prevents rapid identification of problems, and increases space thereby discouraging communication. The true cost of extra inventory is very much in excess of the money tied up in it.

"Just-in-time" (JIT) manufacturing has taught that inventory deliberately hides problems by covering them up. So, perhaps, a quality problem is not considered important because there are always extra parts available if one is defective. JIT encourages deliberate inventory reduction to uncover this sort of problem. Perhaps the safety inventory is deliberately cut. If nothing happens - fine, you have learned to operate with a leaner system. If stoppage occurs - good, because the problem has been recognised and can now be attacked at its root cause.

Examples: inventory exceeding specified quantity limit, so much inventory at workplace that double handling is needed, excessive safety stock.

The Waste of Unnecessary Motions

Unnecessary motions refer to the importance of ergonomics for quality and productivity. If operators have to stretch, bend, pick-up, move in order to see better, or in any way unduly exert themselves, the victim is immediately the operator but ultimately quality and productivity.

This is why an awareness of the ergonomics of the workplace is not only ethically desirable, but economically sound. Toyota, famous for its quality, is known to place a high importance on "quality of worklife". Toyota encourages all its employees to be aware of working conditions that contribute to this form of waste.

Today, of course, this waste is also a health and safety issue.

Examples: bending, reaching, double handling at the workplace, more than two turns to loosen a nut, walking between widely spaced workcentres.

The Waste of Defects

The last, but not least, of Ohno's wastes is the waste of defects. Defects cost money, both immediate and longer term. In Quality Costing the failure or defect categories are internal failure (scrap, rework, delay) and external failure (including warranty, repairs, field service, but also possibly lost custom). Bear in mind that defect costs tend to escalate the longer they remain undetected. Thus a microchip discovered when made might cost just a few Pounds to replace, but if it reaches the customer may cost hundreds, to say nothing of customer goodwill. So, central themes of total quality are "prevention not detection", "quality at source", and "the chain of quality" (meaning that parts per million levels of defect can only be approached by concerted action all along the chain from marketing, to design, to supply, to manufacture, to distribution, to delivery, to field service.) The Toyota philosophy is that a defect should be regarded as a challenge, as an opportunity to improve, rather than something to be traded off against what is ultimately poor management.

In service, "zero defections" has become a powerful theme, recognising that the value of a retained customer increases with time.

Examples: scrap, rework, less than perfect yield, complaints.

The New Wastes

These may be added to Ohno's original list, and are appropriate in service and manufacturing:

The Waste of Untapped Human Potential

Ohno was reported to have said that the real objective of the Toyota Production System was "to create thinking people". So this first of the "new" wastes is directly linked to Ohno, as were the original seven. The 1980s were the decade of factory automation folly. GM and many others learnt the hard and expensive way that the automated factory and warehouse that does not benefit from continuous improvement and ongoing thought is doomed in the productivity race.

Today we have numerous examples, from total quality to self directed work teams, of the power of utilising the thoughts of all employees, not just managers. Of numerous examples, that of Proctor and Gamble which ran several similar factories differentiated only by worker empowerment, is one of the most striking. The "empowered" plants were up to 50% more productive. Several sections of this book, on Open Book Management, on Open Systems, on 5 S, on Self Directed Work Teams, on TPM, have as their foundation the liberation of operator involvement and creativity.

Human potential does not just need to be set free. It requires clear communication as to what is needed (both from management and to management), it requires commitment and support (because uncapping human potential is sometimes seen as a real threat to first line and middle managers), it requires a culture of trust and mutual respect (which cannot be won by mere lofty words, but by example, interest and involvement at the workplace ("Gemba")). Basic education is also necessary. The retort to the question, "What happens if I train them and they go?" should be "What happens if you don't train them and they stay!"

Examples: Not using the creative brainpower of employees, not listening, thinking that only managers have ideas worth pursuing.

The Waste of Inappropriate Systems

Just a few years ago most PCs were 640K and 30 MHz. Today, 12 MB and 150 MHz is hardly adequate to do the same basic jobs (word-processing, spreadsheet, and presentation graphics). Of course, there is no doubt that today's systems can do a whole lot better a whole lot faster. But 20 times better? How much software in your computer is never used (not the packages, but the actual code)? The same goes for MRPII, now repackaged as ERP.

The Lean way is to remove waste before automating, or as Michael Hammer would say "don't automate, obliterate!" The waste of inappropriate systems should not be confined to computers and automation. Indeed, how much record keeping, checking, reconciling, is pure waste? (Recall the categories of waste)

Recently, as more work has been done in supply chains and on business reengineering, the waste of inappropriate systems has been highlighted. Often, it's not the operations that consume the time and the money; it's the paperwork or systems. And we now understand a little more of the dangers of demand amplification, of inappropriate forecasting, and of measurement systems that make people do what is best for them but not best for the company. All this is waste.

Wasted Energy and Water

Energy here refers to sources of power: electricity, gas, oil, coal, and so on. The world's finite resources of most energy sources (except sun and wind) were highlighted in a famous report "The Limits to Growth" written by the Club of Rome in 1970. Their dire predictions have not come to pass, but prices of several sources of energy have risen faster than inflation. Not only are they a significant source of cost for many companies, but there is also the moral obligation of using such resources wisely.

Although energy management systems in factory, office and home have grown in sophistication there still remains the human, common sense element: shutting down the machine, switching off the light, fixing the drip, insulating the roof, taking a full load, efficient routing, and the like. (By the way, the JIT system of delivery does not waste energy when done correctly: use "milkrounds", picking up small quantities from several suppliers in the same area, or rationalise suppliers so as to enable mixed loads daily rather than single products weekly.)

Several companies that have "institutionalised" waste reduction, Toyota included, believe that a good foundation for waste awareness begins with everyday wastes such as electricity. You get into the habit.

Wasted Materials

Today conservation of materials is not only environmentally responsible, but is beginning to be profitable. To reduce the waste of materials a life cycle approach is needed, to conserve materials during design, during manufacture, during customer usage, and beyond customer use in recovery and remanufacturing. See the section on the "R's" of Lean.

Service and Office Wastes

All manufacturers are linked with service operations. Of course, there is waste in service also. In the "back office" most of the above wastes can be applied using a little imagination. Overproduction, for instance, can relate to excess photocopying, wasted food, and excess meetings. Inappropriate processing may relate to excess e mails, copies in triplicate, and over-fancy Powerpoint presentations. However, many service operations are consumed as they are generated, as in phone conversations, so inventory may not be as applicable.

In "front office" operations, customer-related wastes are more relevant. A few of the more important customer service wastes are:

Waste of Customer Time

Where a customer is forced to wait in a queue or to wait for value-adding services. This is primarily a scheduling issue, although providing warning signs such as at Disney World can alleviate this waste. More of this waste occurs where a customer has to provide the same information several times over, as in some visa applications or is asked to provide unnecessary detail. Spike Milligan always insisted that customer surveyors provide him with the same information about themselves as was asked of him.

A sub category of the waste of customer time is the waste of customer inconvenience. Making the customer visit 5 departments to get building plans approved, to have to wait in for a delivery, or to have to travel for a service not offered locally.

Waste of Defecting Customers

A waste that is of increasing concern to service managers is the loss of existing customers. There is a well-known saying, apparently with some justification, that "it costs five time more to acquire a customer as it does to retain one". Having won a customer, make sure that custom is retained.

Further reading:
Taiichi Ohno / Japan Management Association, *Kanban: Just-in-Time at Toyota,* Productivity Press, 1985
James Womack and Daniel Jones, *Lean Thinking,* Simon and Schuster, New York, 1996, ISBN 0-684-81035-2
John Bicheno, *The Quality 60,* PICSIE Books, Buckingham, 1998

The examples are from:
David Brunt and Chris Butterworth, "Waste Elimination in Lean Production - A supply Chain Perspective", Proc ISATA 98, Düsseldorf

The Sustainable Lean Enterprise - The "R's" of Lean

As we begin the new millennium, the 7 wastes or muda, even with the extension of new wastes, are not sufficient in themselves to guide the lean enterprise. Instead what Lovins, Lovins and Hawken term "Natural Capitalism" or the enterprise sustained on a radically more productive use of natural resources is necessary. New Millennium Lean is not only lean on internal operations but on the wider impact on society. The good news is that this can be very profitable.
The 5 R's forms the framework. This allows one to look at Muda through "Green Glasses".

Redesign – Design for the life cycle
➔   for longer product life
➔   for less maintenance during the product lifetime
➔   for ease of recycling the product at the end of its lifetime
➔   using non polluting materials

Reduce – This means reducing the energy and materials
➔   used in manufacture
➔   and used during the life of the product

Recover – The recovery of "waste" is becoming a new priority. This includes
➔   recovery of waste materials such as off cuts and scrap during manufacture
➔   recovery of waste energy during manufacture, for example heat exchangers or recovery of waste steam
➔   recovery of wastes during product use, for example an electric car that recovers energy when going downhill or under braking

Recycle – The recycling of products and components when their life ends. Frequently recycling not only cuts raw material use but also decreases energy use.

Remanufacture – The remanufacture of new products from old products.

All of these are now beginning to make more sense not just environmentally, but economically. Products having longer life and less maintenance compete well - notice the increasing service intervals in cars. Likewise ease of recycling the product and the use of eco-friendly components has become a selling point - or a disincentive where non friendly products are used - remember CFCs. Lovins, Lovins and Hawken cite the example of Interface's Solenium carpet which is made from recycled material, lasts four times longer, and is stain proof and can be water cleaned. Moreover, the carpets are leased to office users and only worn sections are replaced all leading to a 35-fold decrease in the use of materials. The Hypercar uses 85% less fuel and 90% less materials by using composites, improving aerodynamics, by using a hybrid electric drive, and by drive-by-wire. From the manufacturers viewpoint a Hyercar cuts cycle times, part count, assembly effort, and capital needs.

There are interesting parallels with the lean manufacturing principles of under capacity scheduling, avoiding overproduction, and mixed model scheduling. Ranchers are now discovering that the carrying capacity of farms is increased by keeping cattle moving by grazing intensively but briefly at each location, and that by "letting nature's diversity flourish" instead of intensively producing a single crop, yields improve by up to 30%.

Further reading:
Amory Lovins, L Hunter Lovins, Paul Hawken, "A Road Map for Natural Capitalism", *Harvard Business Review,* May-June 1999, pp 145-158

GEMBA

"Gemba" is the workplace. But this Japanese word has taken on significance far beyond its literal translation. Taiichi Ohno, legendary Toyota engineer and father of the JIT system, said "Management begins at the workplace". This whole philosophy can best be captured by the single word: Gemba. Of course, Gemba is by no means confined to the factory.

Contrast the Gemba way with the traditional (Western?) way. The Gemba way is to go to the place of action and collect the FACTS. The traditional way is to remain in the office and to discuss OPINIONS. Gemba can be thought of in terms of the "four actuals": Go to the actual workplace, look at the actual process, observe what is actually happening, collect the actual data.

Gemba is a "mindset thing". Having Gemba means the ability to manage and improve the shopfloor by being at the shopfloor, by learning to see waste, by working with the operators. It is a bias for action, not talk.

Under Gemba, if your organisation has a problem or a decision, go to Gemba first. Do not attempt to resolve problems away from the place of action. Do not let operators come to the manager, let the manager go to the workplace. Spend time on the factory floor or at the service counter. This is the basis of so much Japanese management practice: that new Honda management recruits should spend time working in assembly and in stores, that marketeers from Nikon should spend time working in camera shops, that Toyota sends its Lexus design team to live in California for three months, and so on. Ohno was famous for his "chalk circle" approach - drawing a circle in chalk on the factory floor and requiring a manager to spend several hours inside it whilst observing operations and taking note of wastes. The West too has its devotees: legendary operations teacher Gene Woolsey of Colorado School of Mines requires his graduate students to work alongside the operators before attempting a solution, and as a result has handed out many diamond pins signifying an audited saving of more than $1 million. It is slowly becoming established for Western hotel managers to spend time on the front desk and for senior managers to man complaint lines for a few hours per month. Open plan offices, with senior management sitting right there with "the troops" is Gemba. And, at HP, the production manager's office is on the shop floor.

Some further examples: At a newly established car component factory in England, supervisors were astonished to find they had no office. Their reaction equally astonished their Japanese managers who had assumed that their job was at Gemba! At Toyota, very senior managers spend up to 60% of their total time at Gemba (a figure measured personally by the author). As a result they have deep knowledge of shopfloor operations, equipment, needs, problems, and people. Decision-making is therefore based on first hand knowledge. Moreover, operators know it and appreciate it. Gonick and Smith (quoted by Woolsey) have another example: Ronald Fisher, biologist and father of modern statistics "not only designed and analysed animal breeding experiments, he also cleaned the cages and tended the animals because he knew the loss of an animal would influence his results". True Gemba, although Fisher no doubt never heard the term.

Gemba is, or should be, part of implementation. How often is the Western way based on "change agents", on simulation, on computers or information systems, on classroom based education? These have a place, of course, but Gemba emphasises implementation by everyone, at the workplace, face-to-face, based on in-depth knowledge. And low cost.

Gemba is often combined with other elements. The 5 Whys, Muda (or waste), Hoshin, Kaizen, 5 S, 7 tools, and as a central part of Total Quality. Gemba is the glue for all of these. So today one hears of "Gemba Kanri", "Gemba Kaizen", and "Gemba TPM". The word has already appeared in the English and American dictionary.

FURTHER READING:

Masaaki Imai, *Gemba Kaizen,* McGraw-Hill, New York, 1997, ISBN 0-07-031446-2

Robert E.D. (Gene) Woolsey, "The Fifth Column: The Lieutenant Colonel and Logistics and the Captain and the Chain", *Interfaces,* Vol 26 n 6, Nov/Dec 1996, pp79-81

PLANNING

➡ Scenarios
➡ Time Pacing
➡ Value Focused Thinking
➡ Policy Deployment and Cross Functional Management
➡ Target Costing

SCENARIOS

"Scenarios are plausible, pertinent, alternative stories of the future" (Davis). They can be used for planning and decision making. Scenarios have developed as a powerful alternative or supplement to long term forecasting. As such they can have a dramatic impact on productivity. A great impetus to the use of scenarios has been given by the Royal Dutch Shell Group who have used and developed them to great effect over the past few decades.

Why be concerned about Scenarios in a book on Lean Tools? Because conventional forecasting using extrapolation is more likely to lead to mass manufacture. Scenarios are better at picking up possible discontinuities, thereby encouraging a more flexible, lean approach.

When making longer term plans or decisions, a forecast can be notoriously unreliable (consider the effects and difficulty of predicting the Gulf War, German unification, the financial collapse in the East, or a new and outstandingly successful car from a competitor). So instead use a few scenarios. For instance, most medium and larger companies in the UK should be considering the implications of the matrix of four scenarios, one of which will certainly come to pass: In or out of the Euro, and will the Euro succeed or fail. At Shell, all major projects are judged against two or three scenarios. All projects are expected to demonstrate robustness against all the scenarios. This is a powerful supplement to traditional financial evaluation such as payback or ROI / IRR, where figures are sometimes (always?) massaged. Second, scenarios are used at Shell as a way of learning about the organisation in its environment. In this respect, it is similar to and uses some of the same techniques as System Dynamics (see separate section). The effect is to encourage the use of a strategic perspective at all levels of management. The use of scenarios instead of forecasts is also consistent with "pull" decision-making (starting in the future and working back) rather than "push" (starting from the present and selecting from apparent alternatives). This is further discussed in the section on Value Focused Thinking.

Developing a scenario begins by focusing on those factors that really matter. Then the driving forces that may influence those factors are identified. Collecting information and knowledge on the structure, uncertainties, mental models and what van der Heijden calls the "Business Idea" follows.

The "iceberg" analogy is useful. Events are visible for all to see, but are the manifestation of an invisible structure of developments. These are internal (financial, technological, resource capabilities etc.), external (the "SEPTEMBER" formula of Societal, Economic, Political, Technological, Ecological, Material, Birth (demographics), Environmental, Regulatory), and natural events and laws (such as physics, geological events like earthquakes, etc). Such information must be collected by database or factual search and by interview. The resulting information is then grouped and analysed, for example using Post-it notes.

The concept of the "Business Idea" is important in building scenarios. Any company should have a "distinctive competence" which is the basis of competitive advantage, survival and profit. But distinctive competencies degrade over time. So it is important to understand the business idea which is the feedback loop that allows the business to survive and prosper. Then, scenarios can be developed relating to external events that impact the business idea. For instance, a company may have a competence in the fabrication of steel frames used to support the suspension and engine in cars. This allows the company, with the aid of lean manufacturing techniques and a growing car market, to prosper. So instead of basing plans purely on sales projections, look at some scenarios: the car market declines due to saturation, the particular makes of car which they supply become uncompetitive relative to others, or car makers demand that such suppliers take over responsibility for actual assembly at the car plant itself. According to Davis good scenarios are built from the present, are not easily dismissed, should be internally consistent, and genuinely challenge the user's mental map.

According to van der Heijden there are three ways to build scenarios: Inductive, Deductive and Incremental. The inductive method builds stepwise from existing data, stringing known and chance events together. For instance, in the car example new models may be scheduled at particular points in the future. But perhaps the levels of demand are unknown. A framework of coloured cards (one for each level of demand) mapping new model introduction is laid out. Then an external trend or event (such as given in the previous paragraph) is introduced, and the team doing the scenario strings all the events together. But, each scenario must be defensible. Tight questioning is desirable ("why does that happen?), but destructive criticism ("that's stupid") is not allowed. Also, scenarios must be equally plausible. The test of this is whether the events are worth planning for; an earthquake that destroys the plant is not, unless you live in California or Kobe.

The Deductive method begins by identifying a series of events about which there is uncertainty, and then using this "decision tree" as the framework. For instance in the car example: Do we win the Ford business? If yes, does the market grow? And if yes again, will car manufacturers require first-tier suppliers to assemble on site? The "no" branches are also explored. Probabilities can also be attached to each branch, thereby preventing the exploration of very unlikely scenarios.

The Incremental method simply uses conventional forecasts and projections. This is the "official" view into which, often, considerable time and effort has been sunk. The scenario team then examines this as the baseline, and may question various assumptions and trends. For instance, is a straight-line projection of car sales sustainable? For how long? In this way, "break points" may be established. From these points, alternative stories are developed. Needless to say, this can involve treading on the toes and vested interests of some managers, so the scenario team would be well advised to have top level protection! Like so much planning, it is the process that is at least as important as the actual results. Good scenario planning needs to be redone and updated, examining how to do it better next time.

FURTHER READING:

Kees van der Heijden, *The Art of Strategic Conversation,* John Wiley, Chichester, 1997, ISBN 0-471-96639-8

Pierre Wack, "Scenarios: Uncharted waters ahead", Harvard *Business Review,* Sept/Oct 1985, pp73-90

Pierre Wack, "Scenarios: Shooting the Rapids", Harvard *Business Review,* Nov/Dec 1985, pp131-142

Arie de Geus, *The Living Company,* Nicholas Brealey, London, 1997, ISBN 1-85788-180-X

Ged Davis, "Foreseeing a refracted future", *Scenario Strategy and Planning,* April-May 1999, pp13-15

TIME PACING

"Time pacing" is the undertaking of events such as new product introduction, factory relayout, or staff training at regular intervals. This is as distinct from traditional "event pacing" which waits until action is needed before initiating such change events. Thus, for example, Intel introduces new microprocessors at regular intervals rather than waiting for design breakthroughs or market pressures.

Time pacing is absolutely in line with Lean Operations. It follows the Lean principle of regularity, whereby products are manufactured at regular intervals attempting to make this week's schedule as much like last week's schedule as possible. (See the section on Runners, Repeaters, and Strangers). The advantages are huge; everyone from supplier to operator to marketing knows when a product is due for manufacture. As pointed out, we run our lives on this basis - we don't need a finite scheduler to decide when the family should have breakfast every day. Time pacing is like inventory cycle counting; counting a few parts every day with clear accountability, rather than when the auditors require it and resulting in a panic set of arrangements.

In new product introduction, time pacing cuts development time because each new product is not a complete new adventure, but resources are geared to a momentum to achieve immovable deadlines. Regularity breeds "choreography". It creates a relentless sense of urgency. So new chocolates are introduced in time for Easter, new model cars in time for the Motor Show. And new computer systems in time for the millennium. Moreover, with time pacing planning for the product after next, and the factory after next, has already begun.

Eisenhardt and Brown make the point that there are two related disciplines for Time Pacing. These are Managing Transitions and Managing Rhythm. Both are absolutely in line with good Lean Thinking. Managing Transitions is the process of change management in moving from one product to another. Eisenhardt and Brown say that although new product development is carefully managed, the transition from old to new often is not. Toyota has a whole team that focuses on minimising the waste of materials in moving from one model to another. It introduces new models on the line in a mixed model fashion - first one, then a small batch with space before and after, then a day's run and finally the transition is complete without any stoppage. As this transition process becomes regularised it becomes more routine, better choreographed, less traumatic. The best transition management style sets out to learn from each transition - what went wrong and what can be done better next time.

Managing Rhythms is the process of setting the drumbeat, the frequency with which transitions take place. "Without rhythm, managers tend to be reactive and to see change as an unwelcome surprise" say Eisenhardt and Brown. So this is the task of establishing how frequently batches are run, re-layouts are done, new products introduced, shelf stocking policies reviewed, re-training or job rotation is required, university courses are revisited, or performance is reviewed. The idea is not to be too fast or too slow. Regularity is the key. Capacity must be provided and set aside for this purpose. A programme should be developed which is within the capabilities of the organisation - much like cycle counting again, with A,B,C category frequencies. Eisenhardt and Brown point out that it can be as harmful to increase the frequency of the rhythm as it is to have no rhythm.

Time pacing should become a central strategy for new products, for improvement, for performance review, for personnel development, and the extension of lean. Begin by making a list of activities that can benefit from regularity. Decide the feasible frequency. Then do it, and expect it.

FURTHER READING:
Kathleen Eisenhardt and Shona Brown, "Time Pacing: Competing in Markets that Won't Stand Still", *Harvard Business Review*, March-April 1998, pp 59-69
Kathleen Eisenhardt and Shona Brown, *Competing on the Edge*, Harvard Business School Press, 1998

VALUE FOCUSED THINKING

Clearly, good decision making can have an enormous impact on productivity, speed, and waste. But most decisions are made simply by choosing from a set of apparent alternatives at any time. The danger is that if you always adopt what seems to be the next best thing to do, ultimately you end up with an unfocused mess where waste (or "muda") of all types is endemic. Sound familiar?

With value-based thinking you begin with constraint-free thinking; what you ultimately want to achieve. With the overall concept or vision of where you want to be in (say) 5 years time, you can then work backwards instead of forwards. This is like the kanban pull system rather than traditional push. Make sure that all decisions and changes (whether layout, machines, people, or products) are compatible with this long-term concept.

Take the example of finding a job. You can scan the appointment pages, write off applications and eventually select the best option. This is the traditional, reactive way. Or, you can begin with where you want to be or what you wish to achieve in 10 years. Then you can consider various paths to get there. This will probably open up many more possibilities, some of which you may be able to create yourself by contacting particular employers in particular locations that may allow particular experiences. This is proactive, value focused thinking. The same principles apply in the factory or the office.

Values are simply principles used for evaluation. We should spend time making them explicit through stating objectives. Traditional alternative-based thinking aims at "solving" decision problems. Value focused thinking aims at the identification of decision opportunities, and then with their resolution. So traditional thinking goes through the steps of problem recognition, identification of alternatives, value specification, alternative evaluation, and alternative selection. In value focused thinking the steps are: the specification of strategic objectives, the specification of values, creating decision opportunities, creating alternatives, evaluation and selection.

Remember that the implementation of any decision alternative requires resources of time and money. Spending time on alternatives that appear good in the short term but which are counter-productive in the longer term can waste these. An example is the acquisition of a CNC machining centre which is much faster than machines that it replaces, but creates a bottleneck through which many routings must now pass to keep it occupied. The possibility of cells may be forgone for years to come.

Also, making the longer-term values of both parties' clear opens the possibility for negotiation, and for win-win. You want short lead times; the supplier wants stable orders. Both want profits. So don't talk cost in the short term, think of how both parties can eventually both achieve their objectives by perhaps sharing schedule and design data and by allowing the supplier to take over some fabrication.

Finally, values should be broken down or focused by category. This can create many more alternatives. Begin with the major variables, then break each down by category and match them up. For instance, is it appropriate for all products to go via the same channels? A matrix is often useful; in this case the variables may be cost, service quality, delivery, and time, and the categories could be the markets served - corner shops, pubs, supermarkets, vending machines. Alternatively, two categories of customer size and two categories of needed response time generate four categories each of that may require different distribution channels.

FURTHER READING:
Ralph L Keeney, *Value Focused Thinking: A Path to Creative Decision Making,* Harvard University Press, Cambridge MA, 1992, ISBN 0-674-93198-X (paperback 1996)

POLICY DEPLOYMENT AND CROSS FUNCTIONAL MANAGEMENT

Hoshin (also known as Hoshin Kanri, or Jishu Kanri and in the West as Policy Deployment) and translated as "target plus means", has become a well-accepted way of planning and communicating quality and productivity goals throughout an organisation. It is the emerging method of strategic quality and productivity planning and is used by leading Japanese companies (Toyota, Sony) and by leading Western companies (Hewlett Packard, Texas Instruments, Proctor and Gamble). The objective is to communicate common objectives and gain commitment throughout the organisation.

A "Hoshin" is a word that is increasingly being heard in Western companies, being used to mean the breakthroughs or goals that are required to be achieved so as to meet the overall plan. Thus "what are your hoshins?" means what are the vital few things that you need to focus on. At the top level there may be only 3 to 5 hoshins. But at lower levels, the hoshins form a network or hierarchy of activities that lead to the top-level hoshins. They are developed by consultation. Hoshin goals are customer focused, based on company wide information, and measurable. It is useful in setting these goals to keep in mind the Kano model (see separate section). Kano uses the "Basics, Performance, Delighter" framework. Basics are factors essential for continuing in business, and should have a time dimension, say defect rates now and in three years. Performance factors are areas to gain on competitors by being faster, better, more flexible. Delighters are areas currently not expected by customers but where advantage may be gained.

In essence, according to Juran, there are 5 stages:

→ The business plan is expanded to include quality and productivity goals, not merely profitability and ROI.

→ These goals are deployed down the organisation to determine the required resources, to agree or disagree on the actions, and to fix responsibilities. Deployment means detailed consultation in a climate of trust, communication, and information. (This is frequently referred to as "catchball").

→ Appropriate measures are developed

→ Managers review progress regularly

→ The reward system is adjusted to support the quality and productivity plan.

A useful general framework for Hoshin is that proposed by Rummler and Brache, and discussed in the Improvement section of this book under Business Process Reengineering.

Hoshin operates from a framework of a hierarchy of plans; vision or mission at the top, 3-5 year plans, and annual targets.

Annual Hoshin starts with the concept of homing in on the "vital few". Where there is little change in operating conditions, a company still needs to rely upon departmental management, but top management planning is not required. However, where there is significant change, top management must step in and steer the organisation. ("Hoshin" in Japanese means a compass). This requires strategic planning (for future alignment to identify the vital few strategic gaps), strategy management (for change), and cross-functional management (to manage horizontal business processes). Hoshin is, however, not a planning tool but an execution tool. It deploys the "voice of the customer", not just the profit goals. Typically these goals are cross-functional and relate to major objectives such as cost, quality, delivery, safety, and people.

Departmental management should be relied upon for "kaizen" (i.e. incremental) improvements, but breakthrough improvements which often involve cross functional activities and top level support, should be the focus for Hoshin planning. (We can note here similarities with related fields - Juran talks about the need for project by project improvement to achieve breakthroughs which attack chronic wastes, in BPR Davenport talks about "sequential alteration" between continuous improvement and process reengineering, and in Lean Thinking Womack and Jones discuss kaizen and kaikaku.) See also the section on Continual Improvement.

Once top management has identified the vital few strategic gaps, employees and teams at each level are required to develop plans as to how to close the gaps. This requires that employees have access to adequate up-to-date information - breaking down "confidentiality" barriers found in many Western organisations. There must be a clear link, or cause and effect relationship, between the organisational goals, key objectives, and activities. The employees develop measures, including checkpoints, themselves. At each level, Deming's Plan, Do, Check, Adjust cycle operates. And, there is strong use of both the "7 tools" and the New Tools (see separate sections) to analyse, quantify, and control. Further, root cause analysis, using the 5 Whys method (see separate section), is used at each level.

The Hoshin concept can be seen as two stages: Planning for Focus and Planning for Achievement. In the Focus stage thinking about the 3 to 5 year plan leads to identification of critical success factors and the "vital few" upon which to concentrate. Then in the Achievement stage, breakthrough goals are developed for the vital few areas, which are expanded out into annual targets, which in turn lead to the necessary projects and actions. Top management should be concerned with developing the "vision". But, unlike many western companies, this vision is translated into required actions. One way is to use "backward planning" - starting with the ideal design and working backwards, year by year, to identify the constraints that need to be eliminated.

Hoshin uses the "outcome, what, how, how much, and who" framework. At Board level, a visioning process covers the key questions of what is to be the required outcome for the company (e.g. 10% growth), what is to be achieved (e.g. reductions in lead time), how is it to be done (e.g. extend lean manufacturing principles), and how much (all shops to be on JIT by year end). Specific quality and productivity goals are established. Then, the "who" are discussed. Normally there will be several managers responsible for achieving these objectives. Appropriate measures are also developed.

The objective cascading process of Hoshin is also different to most traditional models. In traditional plan cascading plans come down from the top without consultation, and there is little vertical and especially horizontal alignment. In Hoshin, people who must implement the plan, design the plan. The means, not just the outcomes, must be specified. And there are specific and ongoing checks to see that local plans add up to overall plans.

At each level a group meeting takes place. This is referred to as "Catch Ball" (ideas are tossed around like a ball) or "Huddles". Ideas flow from all directions, and consensus and negotiation, not authority, arrive at agreement. If a goal is really infeasible the upper tier is informed. (See similarities with Open Book Management). A Japanese word for this is the "Ringi" system.

Feedback goes in the reverse direction. Difficulties and constraints are identified and fed back to the level above who are required to act accordingly. Also, measures are taken and gaps identified. If a problem is identified, corrective action is taken in relation to the process, not the person. This "blame free" culture is vital.

A final stage in the cycle is the Hoshin Audit where achievements against plan are formally rolled up the organisation. Exceptions are noted and carried forward. Hewlett Packard does this very formally once per quarter, "flagging up" (by yellow or red "flag") problem areas. Intel uses, against each Hoshin, a classification showing highlights, lowlights, issues, and plans. Again, root causes are identified. Audits can be quite frequent – quarterly or monthly.

Hoshin is in essence an expanded form of "team briefing" but requires written commitment, identification of goals, the setting of measures, and discussion at each level. In Western companies, top management sometimes spends much time on corporate vision but then fails to put in place a mechanism to translate the vision into deliverables and measures, at each level in the organisation. Hoshin may go some way to explaining why in Japanese companies the decision making process is slower, but implementation is much faster and smoother.

CROSS FUNCTIONAL MANAGEMENT (CFM)

According to JUSE (1988) "Cross Functional Management is a process designed to encourage and support interdepartmental communication and co-operation throughout a company, as opposed to command and control through narrow departments and divisions. The purpose is to attain such company-wide targets as quality, cost and delivery of products and services by optimising the share of work". In other words CFM attempts to implement the process view of organisation, strongly associated with TQM and BPR. It fits in well with Hoshin using the same policy deployment methodology, but emphasises measurement and management of major objectives on a cross functional basis. Long employed in Japan, CFM is also found at HP, Deere and AT&T.

LEAN IMPLEMENTATION AND CFM

When selecting appropriate approaches, say from this book, a matrix can be used. The major goals (perhaps cost, quality, delivery, safety, time to market, flexibility) form the rows, each with a clear time-specific target. The columns are the programs (perhaps SMED, single piece flow, TPM, cells, mapping, 5S, supplier development). The cells of the matrix are used to make a judgement as to the effectiveness of each approach on each goal. Simply use high, medium, low, nil. This helps to guide priorities.

At Lean Enterprise Research Centre Cardiff Business School, a "top hat" is added to this matrix. This is exactly like the "roof" of a QFD diagram. The triangular matrix sits on top of the techniques and identifies any potential clashes. See the figure.

Cross Functional Management Matrix

impacts are indicated by H=high, M=medium, L=low

FURTHER READING:

Y. Akao, *Hoshin Kanri: Policy Deployment for Successful TQM,* Productivity Press, Portland, 1991

Michele L Bechtell, *The Management Compass: Steering the Corporation Using Hoshin Planning,* AMA Management Briefing, New York, 1995

R G Lee and Barry Dale, "Policy Deployment: An Examination of the Theory", *Int Jnl of Quality and Reliability Management,* Volume 15 No 5, 1998, pp520-540

Note: Nick Rich of Cardiff Business School is due to publish a book in this area in 2000. It will be good.

TARGET COSTING

Consider the equation:
Cost   +   Profit   =   Price

It is traditional to start with the product cost and add a percentage for profit to derive the price. Target costing, however, begins with the price that it is considered possible to achieve, and subtracts a percentage for profit to derive the target cost. Target Cost = Market Price – target profit.

We may notice a few points:

→   Target costing is done ahead of time. It has to anticipate future customer willingness to pay, and the market size. There is risk and uncertainty involved.

→   Target costing begins with the customer and the market, not with engineer or designer.

→   Target costing is closed-ended, not open-ended, and so is a tough system to work to.

→   It is a proactive, not a reactive, system.

Target costing has as its partner Value Engineering that has as its aim the retention of product functionality at a reduced or target cost. Also, ideas from mass customisation and product platforms are also very relevant In achieving the target cost, QFD and DFM (Design for Manufacture) are both relevant. Finally, concurrent or simultaneous engineering is invariably adopted alongside target costing. See the separate sections on all these topics.

According to Cooper and Slagmulder, target costing has the cardinal rule "The target cost of a product can never be exceeded". Unless this rule is in place a target costing system will lose its effectiveness and will always be subject to the temptation of adding just a little bit more functionality at a little higher price.

For strategic reasons there may be very little relationship between product costs and product price. An outstanding recent example is Toyota's Prius that runs on both electricity and petrol. According to Business Week, The Prius price is $17k but may cost twice as much. (Business Week, 15 Dec 1997, p35)

There are two main stages to target costing, establishing target costs and attaining target costs. Establishing target costs comes from allowable cost and target profit margin. Much of the following material on the three strands is derived from Cooper and Slagmulder and Ansari et al.

Allowable cost is the maximum cost at which a product must be made so as to earn its target profit margin. The allowable cost is derived from target selling price - target profit margin. Target selling price is determined from three factors: customers, competitive offerings, and strategic objectives. The price customers can be expected to pay depends importantly upon their perception of value. So if a new product or variant is proposed, marketing must determine if and how much customers are prepared to pay for the new features. The position on the product life cycle is important (an innovative lead product may be able to command a higher price). Customer loyalty and brand name are influential. Then there are the competitive offerings: what functions are being, and are anticipated to be, offered at what prices. Finally there are strategic considerations as to, for example whether the product is to compete in a new market, and the importance of market share. Side by side with allowable costing go the Design Trilogies of cost, time, and quality, and of price, quality, and functionality. There may be tradeoffs within each of these groups. In the experience of the author of this book, time is often a dominant consideration that may push up the allowable cost.

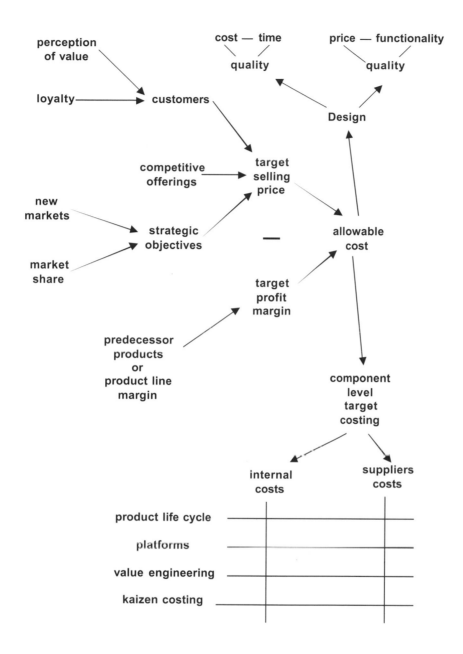

Target profit margin is the next factor in determining allowable cost. There are two approaches, according to Cooper and Slagmulder. The first uses the predecessor product and adjusts for market conditions. The second starts with the margin of the whole product line, and makes adjustments according to market conditions.

Attaining target costs should begin as soon as possible and will overlap with the establishment of target costs stage. A central tool is value engineering, a topic that is dealt with in a separate section. Suffice it to say here that value engineering should be strongly related to customer requirements, cutting costs in areas of low customer value but improving functionality in areas of high customer value. A useful concept is the Waste Free Cost. This is the cost assuming that all avoidable waste or MUDA has been taken out. Refer to the section on Lean Thinking for a view on these wastes. Another guiding principle is the "cardinal rule" that cost must not be allowed to creep up: if an extra function is added, there must be a compensating cost reduction elsewhere. The process of moving in increments from the current cost to the target cost is referred to as "drifting" and is closely monitored. Once the target cost has been achieved, effort stops: there is no virtue in achieving more than is required.

Importantly, attaining target costs involves looking right across the product life cycle (including distribution, service and final disposal) and both inside and outside costs. In other words the company and its suppliers and distributors should be involved. This is because, at the concept and design stage, a company locks in perhaps 80% of future costs.

(By the way, in aircraft and racing car design, a governing target factor is weight, less so cost. Many of the same methods apply.)

Component Level Target Costing. In product level target costing, often assumptions on component costs have to be made. This is particularly the case for a complex product or a product involving new technology. The concept of supplier partnerships is highly relevant; that is working closely with a few core suppliers, and in early involvement in decision making. Teams of engineers from the main product company may assist suppliers in cost reduction activities, particularly value engineering. The Bose Corporation concept of "JIT II" may be particularly helpful (see the section on Supplier Partnership). Sometimes this stage is broken down by tier, with first tier suppliers being responsible for cost achievement targets for major subassemblies. Of course, the Pareto principle is always relevant: spend more time on more expensive components. In some cases, component costs are critically dependent upon volume; in this case the parent product company may consider issuing guarantees, may purchase equipment on leaseback or may guarantee the material cost differences.

Once the product goes into production, three other actions may follow:

➔ Further variants may be launched from the base product or platform at strategic intervals, to maintain competitiveness by either adding functionality or to pass on advances in technology, or to pass on price reductions. See the section on Product Platforms.

➔ Further value engineering (sometimes referred to as value analysis after the initial launch) may take place at regular intervals. One Japanese company aims to do a value analysis on each of their continuing consumer electronics products once per year. The aim is to either reduce cost or improve functionality.

➔ "Kaizen costing" is undertaken. Kaizen costing is the post-launch version of target costing, and aims to achieve target cost levels at specific points in the future. This overlaps with value analysis. It targets both the product design and the process design. Specific teams are charged with the objective - it is not a chance activity relying on operator suggestions. This is a form of Lean Strategy.

FURTHER READING:
Robin Cooper and Regine Slagmulder, *Target Costing and Value Engineering,* Institute of Management Accountants / Productivity Press, Portland, OR, 1997, ISBN 1-56327-172-9
Robert Kaplan and Robin Cooper, *Cost and Effect,* Harvard Business School Press, Boston, MA, 1998, ISBN 0-87584-788-9
Shahid Ansari et al, *Target Costing,* Irwin/McGraw Hill, 1997, ISBN 0-256-27145-2

DESIGN AND NEW PRODUCTS

- ➡ Development Time and Organising for New Products
- ➡ Four Objectives and Six Trade-offs
- ➡ Simultaneous and Concurrent Engineering
- ➡ Mass Customisation and Modularity
- ➡ Design for Manufacture
- ➡ Product Platforms
- ➡ Four Fields Mapping
- ➡ Quality Function Deployment
- ➡ TRIZ
- ➡ Concept Screening

Good design management is essential in lean operations because perhaps 90% of costs may be locked in after the design stage. Also, the time taken to bring a new design or product to market is where much of the competitive edge is gained or lost. In this section, organisational concepts, tradeoffs, and some planning tools are looked at.

DEVELOPMENT TIME AND ORGANISING FOR NEW PRODUCTS

Two central issues in design are how is it organised and how is time reduced or optimised. The following are a few observations.

Smith and Reinertsen stress that development time should be thought of beginning at the time of identifying need, not at the start of the design and development cycle. This is much the same as attacking the manufacturing lead time, when most time is being consumed in order booking. Management dither on approving the start of development is often the major opportunity for time reduction.

As time progresses:

→   Market opportunity decreases

→   The sense of urgency increases

→   Project spending increases, exponentially

→   Opportunity to save future costs, in manufacturing and use, decreases

→   In traditional new product development, marketing, then engineering, then manufacturing tends to dominate. However, with full-time staffing from these functions, the staff is forced to co-operate more evenly through time.

The established approach of "gateways" or phases, through which a new product must pass, is acceptable for large projects but questionable for most smaller projects. The problem is that, in a fast moving world, delays to evaluate technical risk allows market opportunity to slip by. Overlapping should be used where possible. The phased approach with the sequence following a flowchart structure with decision points should be replaced by a "truss" structure. Here the functional activities (marketing, engineering, etc) are arranged in layers with cross-functional linkages between the activities. (See also 4 Fields Mapping)

On Tooling, Womack, Jones and Roos suggested firming up on tooling as design progresses, rather than waiting for hand-over to engineering. Smith and Reinertsen suggest three approaches:

→   Easing into production with partially tooled products

→   Invest in tooling speculatively

→   Use soft tooling (quickly fabricated, easily modified) for early production, and only later invest in durable tooling.

The selection of tooling strategy depends upon several factors including the importance of time, the nature of the processes, and the risk of change.

Cusumano and Nobeoka point out four approaches to product development.

→   New designs where a product or platform is designed from scratch (Renault for example).

→   Concurrent technology transfer which uses a platform from another ongoing project (Honda and Toyota, for example).

→   Sequential technology transfer which uses a platform from an established design (Chrysler, for example).

→   Design modification involves modifying the design of a predecessor.

Three shifts in organisation have occurred. The first was from functional, sequential management to one-at-a-time, overlapping and integrated projects (called "Lean") which concentrated on time. Then to multi-projects concentrating more on value and costs, and finally to multi-firm, multi-projects ("beyond Lean").

Both Cusumano and Nobeoka, and Smith and Reinertsen, amongst others, discuss the old chestnut of the organisation of design and development. Functional "silo" organisation is now passé. The question remains as to whether a lightweight project manager, a balanced (matrix) organisation, a heavyweight project manager (who dominates functional managers) or a separate team ("skunk works") is best. Smith and Reinertsen seem to plump for a mix between a matrix for stable developments and separate teams. The matrix form was still the favoured style in the majority of car manufacturers in the mid 1990's, but significantly not used by Toyota, Ford, Nissan, or Honda. Womack and Jones seem to favour the heavyweight manager style but with staff reverting to functional departments for updating and rejuvenation between projects. Cusumano and Nobeoka, illustrating their case with Toyota, say that there is now evolution beyond single project heavyweight project management to multi-project organisation that is a complex of project organisations and engineering and planning divisions. However, they warn that this is probably for major corporations only.

Cusumano and Nobeoka's conclusion is that it is better to leverage investment in technology transfer (for instance through multi-product management and the use of platforms) than to not do so. Also to leverage quickly across markets (concurrent transfer) is better than slowly across time (sequential transfer).

Sobek et al have shown how Toyota has made subtle adjustments or twists to the evolving wisdom of new product development. For instance, Toyota uses "mentoring supervisors" to guide development work, to avoid the compromise between strong functional experts and facilitating cross-functional managers who are not experts. By using mentors who are skilled engineers, designers benefit both from freedom and from accumulated knowledge. In another twist, Toyota uses "chief engineers" as compromise between functional management and heavyweight project managers as the leaders for new products. These chief engineers are highly skilled engineers, having both the technical knowledge and ability to see the whole picture, but nevertheless operate by persuasion rather than authority. Job rotation takes place within functions for inexperienced engineers, but between functions at senior levels. Toyota also apparently avoids the pitfalls of the highly standardised gateway process (which always seem to need revision) favoured by many Western companies. Instead, Toyota uses a simplified standardised work plan that relies upon "intense socialisation" built up in early years. The standards are built up by the engineers themselves, rather than by a centralised function. For instance, when an engineer learns something new, the knowledge is incorporated into checklists against which all future designs are evaluated.

FURTHER READING:

Michael Cusumano and Kentaro Nobeoka, *Thinking Beyond Lean,* The Free Press, New York, 1998, ISBN 0-684-84918-6

Durward Sobek, Jeffrey Liker, Allen Ward, "Another Look at How Toyota Integrates Product Development", *Harvard Business Review,* July-August 1998, pp36-49

Preston Smith and Donald Reinertsen, *Developing Products in Half The Time,* Van Nostrand Reinhold, New York, 1991, ISBN 0-442-00243-2

Four Objectives and Six Trade-offs

In their ground breaking work on accelerated new product development, Smith and Reinertsen identified four objectives (Development Speed, Product Cost, Product Performance, and Development Programme Expense) as being central to the management of new product development. These four areas interact in six ways. Smith and Reinertsen believe that it is necessary to quantify these trade-offs, since every new product development is a compromise that needs to be understood and managed.

Development Speed and Product Cost. Rationalising and improving a design through part count, weight analysis, part commonality, DFM, and value engineering can save future costs. But they take time, thereby delaying the introduction of the product and possibly loosing market share.

Development Speed and Product Performance: Likewise, improving a design can make it more attractive to customers thereby improving future sales through a larger market, a higher price, and a longer product life. These improvements take time, again sacrificing initial sales and initial market share.

Development Speed and Development Programme Expense: This is the traditional "project crashing" trade-off from classic project management. Most projects have "fixed" costs such as management and overhead that accumulate with time. On the other hand, within limits, adding extra resources decreases project duration but costs more. Is it worthwhile spending more to finish earlier?

Product Cost and Product Performance: Adding or redesigning a feature will increase cost, but may improve performance. What sales increase will the improved performance result in?

Product Cost and Development Programme Expense: By spending more on development, say through value engineering, we may be able to reduce cost. Is it worth it?

Development Programme Expense and Product Performance: Improving a design and improving performance may result in improved sales. But improving performance may involve additional cost.

Smith and Reinertsen suggest that a simple spreadsheet model be developed to quantify these six relationships. Remember to use the time value of money, trading off immediate project costs against discounted future sales. Quantifying the six relationships forces marketing, design and engineering to think carefully about additions and rationalisations. Play around with the sensitivity. Clearly, as Michael Cusumano and Kentaro Nobeoka show in their comparisons of Japanese approaches to car development between 1980 and 1990, the best answers to these tradeoffs have changed and are likely to continue changing. That is the benefit of clarifying the six trade-offs.

Further reading:
Michael Cusumano and Kentaro Nobeoka, *Thinking Beyond Lean,* The Free Press, New York, 1998, ISBN 0-684-84918-6
Preston Smith and Donald Reinertsen, *Developing Products in Half The Time,* Van Nostrand Reinhold, New York, 1991, ISBN 0-442-00243-2

SIMULTANEOUS AND CONCURRENT ENGINEERING

Simultaneous or Concurrent Engineering (the words are interchangeable, sometimes depending on American or British usage) is an established Lean Technique. The idea is for all relevant parties in a product introduction to work concurrently on the project. This is in contrast to the traditional practice of sequential design, where the design for a new product is "thrown over the wall" to the next department, thereby resulting in what Womack and Jones refer to as batch and queue processing. Traditional practice is organised around strong functional departments (marketing, R&D, design, engineering, production, manufacturing, materials management, quality, logistics and distribution). Typically these functions do not share the same priorities, and interpret the requirements differently. Each may try to "optimise" the design from their own perspective, but as a result suboptimising the general product in relation to the customer and the product life cycle. A now-classic cartoon shows the development of a swing as it moves through the various functions, moving further and further away from the customer's requirement. Not only that, it is also slow, usually with numerous rework loops. Failure mode analysis and legal considerations may result in yet further delay.

Simultaneous Engineering uses a strong product champion or project leader and a matrix form of structure. The real power is vested in the project leader rather than the functional department heads. The project manager often holds budget responsibility, and staff reports to her or him in the first instance. A critical arrangement is co-location of the team. Close proximity allows instant resolution of problems and a single clear view of requirements. There may still be gateways or sign-offs through which the design must pass, but such approvals are best done in a committee of functional heads, rather than one at a time. Although staff is seconded from functional departments to the project team, they return to the functional department at the end of the project and may call on functional expertise during the project. The functional head typically retains the responsibility for maintaining the up-to-date skills of his staff and databases. Generally, in traditional practice there is little involvement with suppliers in the design process, although there is also the concept of "open specifications" whereby a supplier is given the broad spec and asked to come up with the detail.

The project manager controls the budget and can contract in staff from functional departments and outside firms, as is deemed necessary.

Simultaneous / Concurrent engineering is further aided by technology: common CAD and simulation software is used within the team and may also be used externally (see the section on Agile and Virtual manufacturing), stereo lithography may be use for three dimensional visualisation and for tool path, tool and die design and manufacturing analysis. Group Technology, Product Platform and Mass Customisation principles may all be used (see separate sections on each of these).

The simultaneous engineering approach described here is referred to by Ward et al as a so-called "point based process". Although a team based approach and excellent common software may be used, the design moves in approved stages from styling, to system design, to component design, to manufacturing engineering, to maintenance planning, and at each point or stage the design is frozen before moving ahead.

By contrast, Toyota uses an approach referred to by Ward et al as a "set based approach". Ward gives the analogy of setting up a meeting. One alternative is for an overall organiser to select date and time, then negotiate with a second participant and if necessary revise, then with a third, revising yet again if necessary, and so on. This represents the traditional form of design. Concurrent engineering can be used to shorten the process by either having a short meeting to decide when the longer one is to be held, or have the more powerful participants pre-decide the time, and then force the others to attend at that time. This is equivalent to the strong project manager form of concurrent engineering.

The set based approach (or Toyota) system requires participants to submit times when they are available, subject to certain constraints, and then determining the best intersection. Toyota uses broad constraints or checklists of infeasible designs but allows suppliers and internal designers to suggest their own alternatives. The most important supplier partners can not only influence component design but also the whole car concept. Second level (not necessarily tier) suppliers wait for Toyota to define the needs but then work with Toyota to define component designs. Third level suppliers' design to specification or use Toyota's own design. Throughout the process there is a constant two-way negotiation process. The amount of communication, however, appears to be less than with traditional concurrent engineering. Because of the high degree of trust between partners, manual milestones rather than computer-based project management software is used. Within the milestones there is considerable individual flexibility.

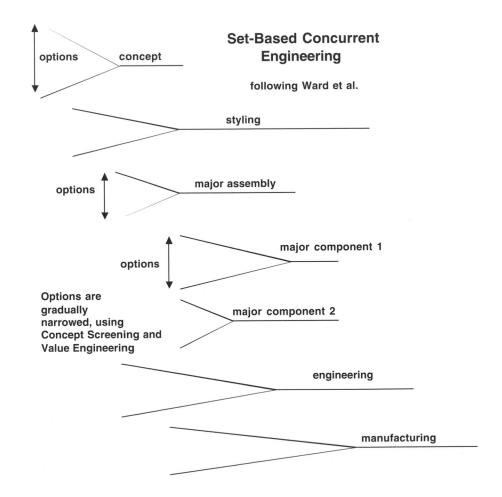

The Toyota process follows a set-narrowing procedure as shown in the figure overleaf. Concepts are gradually narrowed using "Concept Screening" techniques (see separate section). Note: there are similarities with the "Production Variety Funnel" maps described in the section on Value Stream Mapping.

Possible "solution sets" are explored in parallel, but once a particular solution is decided upon it is frozen unless a change is absolutely necessary. This is similar to the JIT manufacturing concept of "variety as late as possible" - delaying freezing specifications until the last possible moment.

While car design is proceeding, engineering and die production also proceeds. During the early concept stages, engineering makes from 5 to 20 one-fifth scale clay models. The engineering team begins full-scale clay modelling at intermediate stages as well as at final stage, unlike other car manufacturers who only make half size models during early stages. This enables tool and die designers to begin work. They too use engineering check sheets, built up from experience, about what can and cannot be done. Difficulties are fed back immediately to the design team.

All this may sound unduly complicated and inefficient. In fact, by keeping its options open, flexibility is maximised, enabling Toyota to bring cars to market in 27 months with 500 people as opposed to Chrysler's 37 months with 750 people (1995 figures). Not only is design fast and efficient, but decision making is also more data-based and allows suppliers to contribute their own expertise far more than in conventional design. Other companies both in manufacturing and in service can use these principles used by Toyota.

Metrics in Concurrent Engineering

The old phrase "what gets measured gets done" is valid in Concurrent Engineering also. It is important that project teams are subject to a number of metrics (a) for which they all are jointly responsible, and (b) which bind the project team together. Measures should be developed for cost, quality, time, and perhaps innovation, safety, and people. Examples are number of design iterations, number of changes after production has started, time to first off and time to break even, time to make a design modification, and ability to meet target costs.

Further Reading:

Allen Ward, Jeffrey Liker, John Cristano, Durward Sobek, "The Second Toyota Paradox: How Delaying Decisions Can Make Better Cars Faster", *Sloan Management Review,* Vol 36, No 3, Spring 1995, pp 43-61

James Womack, Daniel Jones, Daniel Roos, *The Machine that Changed the World,* Rawson Associates, New York, 1990, Chapter 5, ISBN 0-89256-350-8

John Wesner, Jeffrey Haitt, David Trimble, *Winning with Quality: Applying Quality Principles in Product Development,* Addison Wesley, Reading MA, 1995, ISBN 0-201-63347-7

Preston Smith and Donald Reinertsen, *Developing Products in Half The Time,* Van Nostrand Reinhold, New York, 1991, ISBN 0-442-00243-2

Durward Sobek, Jeffrey Liker, Allen Ward, "Another Look at How Toyota Integrates Product Development", *Harvard Business Review,* July-August 1998, pp36-49

MASS CUSTOMISATION AND MODULARITY

Mass Customisation aims at the mass production of customised products and services, thus producing at low cost but with high, or even infinite, variety. These goals have traditionally been considered contradictory. However, Joseph Pine has articulated the methods and types of mass customisation and shown that, in many businesses both are now possible. The trend seems inevitable. Modularity is a special case of mass customisation (or perhaps vice versa) and would seem to be the prime organising principle for the agile, networked companies that are now emerging.

Since mass customisation involves producing a product or service uniquely for each customer, the customer must be involved in design at some stage. Duray and Milligan point out that this can happen at any of five stages. At the design stage, a product is uniquely designed for each customer. Taditional project engineering does this of course, but this is not mass customisation. It is mass customisation where the customer can select from a standard set of features which nevertheless allow uniqueness. An example is a signwriter where a customer can select from standard patterns but make his own wording. At the fabrication stage mass custimisation involves altering components to customer specification. An example is the one-stop lensmakers that are becoming common. Mass customisation at the assembly stage involves the selection and arrangement of components to customer specification. The supreme example is Dell's configuring of PC systems to customer requirement, often over the internet. Finally post production mass customisation involves the customer in configuring his ownproduct himself. Examples are Lego bricks, and selecting own software or hi-fi components.

Pine also discusses five methods for mass customisation with different emphasis.

CUSTOMISE SERVICES AROUND STANDARD PRODUCTS OR SERVICES. Although standard products are used, customisation takes place at the delivery stage. For example, airline passengers may be offered different meals or in-flight entertainment, and pizza customers are offered substantial choice. On the Internet it is possible to receive a customised news service. Standard hotel rooms may nevertheless be offered in non-smoking, secretarial support, quiet-during-day, or close-to-entertainment or pool varieties. Customisation through service may be used, for instance through individual support of a standard computer or through knowledge of the specific requirements of individual customers using a dry cleaner. The key to this method is good information on customer, especially repeat customer, needs.

CREATE CUSTOMISABLE PRODUCTS AND SERVICES. Here, customisation is designed into standard products which customers tailor for themselves. Examples are adjustable office chairs, automatically adjustable seats, steering wheels or even gearing on some cars, or the flexible razor which automatically adjusts to the user's face. The key here is often technology, but technology that follows customer need. The automatic teller machine offering a variety of services is a prime example.

POINT OF DELIVERY CUSTOMISATION. Here variety is built in just prior to delivery, even later than the first type of customisation. For instance, software specific to a customer's requirements may be added. In-store point of delivery customisation - spectacles, photo developing, quick-fit tyres - are now commonplace. This type of customisation often requires "raw material" or semi-processes inventory to be held at the point of delivery, but the advantage is zero finished goods inventory and improved speed of response.

QUICK RESPONSE. Quick response usually involves integration along much of the supply chain. A classic example is Benetton's "jerseys in grey" which are kept undyed until actual demand is communicated, often via electronic data interchange (EDI), and supplied on a quick delivery service. Inventory is only kept in a partly processed state at a central factory, none in the distribution chain, and a minimum is kept in shops. (By the way, Quick Response is also known as Efficient Consumer Response, the former associated with apparel, and the latter with groceries.)

MODULARITY. This long-established form of customisation simply involves assembly to order from standard modules. Examples are legion: calculators or cars having different appearance but sharing the same "platform", aeroplanes, and many restaurant meals. Pine lists six types: "Component sharing", where variety of components is kept to a minimum by using Group Technology (see separate section). Design for Manufacture (see separate section). "Component swapping" (cars with different engines). "Cut-to-fit modularity" (a classic example being made to order bicycles). "Mix modularity", combining several of the above, and "bus modularity", where components, such as on a hi-fi are linked together. Baldwin and Clark take this further, believing modularity to be a fundamental organising principle for the future. Thus today Delphi (a GM company) makes the complete driver's cockpit for Mercedes, and VW runs a truck factory using not only the modules of suppliers but their operators also.

Pine suggests the well-known (Rudyard Kipling) framework for approaching customisation: the who, what, when, where, why, and how. This amounts to detail on market segmentation. Take a hotel example: who are the customers (businessmen and tourists), what do they need (support and leisure), when (daytime and evening), why (working away from home, having a break), where (customised by location), how (focused hotels? separate blocks? secretarial support for business, video for tourists, etc).

Gilmore and Pine (1997) have gone on to state that there are four approaches to customisation. "Collaborative customizers" work with customers in understanding or articulating their needs (a wedding catering service), "adaptive customizers" offer standard but self-adjusting or adapting products or services (offering hi-fi, or car seats which the customer adjusts), "cosmetic customizers" offer standard products but present them differently (the same product is offered but in customer specified sizes, own-labels), and "transparent customizers" take on the customisation task themselves often without the customer knowing (providing the right blend of lubricant to match the seasons or the wear rate).

Yet a further type of mass customisation is to do with "platforms". See the separate section on this topic.

What is valuable about these classifications is their stimulation of thinking. Today customers are increasingly demanding for both tailoring of solutions as well as low cost. Mass customisation is the way to go.

FURTHER READING:
B. Joseph Pine, *Mass Customisation,* Harvard Business School Press, Boston, MA, 1993
James H. Gilmore and B. Joseph Pine, "The Four Faces of Mass Customisation", *Harvard Business Review,* Jan/Feb 1997, pp 91-101
Carliss Baldwin and Kim Clark, "Managing in an age of Modularity", *Harvard Business Review,* Sept-Oct, 1997, pp84-93
Rebecca Duray and Glenn Milligan, "Improving Customer Satisfaction Through Mass Customisation", *Quality Progress,* August 1999, pp60-66

DESIGN FOR MANUFACTURE

Design for manufacture (DFM) is a key "enabling" concept for lean manufacture. Easy and fast assembly has an impact right through the manufacturing life of the product, so time spent up front is well spent. A wider view of DFM should consider the cost of components, the cost and ease of assembly, and the support costs.

Cost of Components should be the starting point. Much will depend upon the envisaged production volume: for instance, machined components may be most cost effective for low volumes, pressings (requiring tooling investment) best for middle volumes, and mouldings (requiring even higher initial investment but low unit costs) best for higher volumes. Other issues to do with the cost of components include sourcing and supplier partnership issues (to what extent is the design done in-house or will it be "black boxed"), the use of group technology (G.T. - see separate section) perhaps trading off weight against the cost of common parts.

Variety as late as possible, and Platforms. Variety as late as possible aims to preserve manufacturing variety options to as late as possible along the manufacturing sequence. This again trades off optimal performance from a design perspective, against reductions in inventories and manufacturing flexibility. Similarly, common "platforms" may be used. Audi and VW Golf share platforms, as do many Japanese calculators often varying considerably in price. The Apple Macintosh uses the platform of a common operating system (MacOS) and common microprocessors (the G3 processor) for a variety of computers.

COMPLEXITY OF ASSEMBLY

Boothroyd and Dewhurst have suggested a DFA index aimed at assessing the complexity of assembly. This is the ratio of (the theoretical minimum number of parts x 3 seconds) to the estimated total assembly time. The theoretically minimum number of parts can be calculated by having each theoretical part meet at least one of the following:

➔   Does the part need to move relative to the rest of the assembly?

➔   Must the part be made of a different material?

➔   Does the part have to be physically separated for access, replacement, or repair?

If not theoretically necessary, then the designer should consider the physical integration with one or more other parts. And why 3 seconds? Merely because that is a good average unit assembly time. Once this is done, then Boothroyd and Dewhurst suggest further rules for maximum ease of assembly. These are:

➔   Insert part from the top of the assembly

➔   Make part self-aligning

➔   Avoid having to orient the part

➔   Arrange for one-handed assembly

➔   No tools are required for assembly

➔   Assembly takes place in a single, linear motion

➔   The part is secured immediately upon insertion

Boothroyd and Dewhurst now market a software package to assist with DFM.

Boothroyd and Dewhurst go on to suggest that for both DFA and Design Complexity (see below), not only should there be measurement and monitoring of one's own products, but that the measures should be determined for competitor's products as well. This is a form of benchmarking. Targets should be set. Such measures should also be used for value engineering. Continuous improvement is therefore driven by specific targets, measures, and benchmarks, and not left to chance.

It should be possible to create design and assembly indices for each subassembly, to rank them by complexity, and Pareto fashion to tackle complexity systematically. Further, it should be possible to determine, from benchmarking competitor products, the best of each type of assembly and then to construct a theoretical overall best product even though one may not yet exist in practice. This is a form of Stuart Pugh's "Concept Screening" method (see separate section).

Assembly Support Costs should be considered at the design stage. This includes consideration of:

→ Inventory management and sourcing

→ The necessity for new vendors

→ A requirement for new tools to be used

→ A requirement for new operator skills to be acquired

→ The possibility of failsafing

As a useful supplement on design, David Norman, an American psychologist, urges designers to consider the manufacturing and assembly errors that do occur, and make them easier to correct. This should be done at the design stage. He further urges designers to take a wider view of users. "Think of an object's user as attempting to do a task, getting there by imperfect approximations." So it's the usefulness of the product in its wider context that counts.

COMPLEXITY OF DESIGN

Boothroyd and Dewhurst have also suggested a measure for the assessment of design complexity. They use three factors: the number of parts (Np), the number of types of parts (Nt), and the number of interfaces between parts (Ni). First, the numeric value of each of these factors is determined by addition. Then, the factors are multiplied and the cube root taken. This yields the design complexity factor. Note that reducing the number of parts usually also reduces the number of interfaces, which are points at which defects and difficulties are most common. Also, reducing the number of types of part has a direct impact upon inventory management and quality.

OTHER TYPES

"Design for" is not limited to "assembly" (DFA) or "manufacture" (DFM). There are other types too: Design for Performance (DFP), Design for Testability (DFT), Design for Serviceability (DFS), and Design for Compliance (DFC). No doubt others too. Collectively they are known as DFX.

FURTHER READING:

G. Boothroyd and P. Dewhurst, *Product Design for Assembly Handbook,* Boothroyd Dewhurst Inc., Wakefield, RI, 1987

Karl Ulrich and Steven Eppinger, *Product Design and Development,* McGraw Hill, New York, 1995, Chapter 3

David Norman, *The Design of Everyday Things,* Doubleday, New York, 1989.

PRODUCT PLATFORMS

A product platform is a design from which many derivative designs or products can be launched, often over an extended period. So, instead of designing each new product one at a time, a product platform concept is worked out which leads to a family of products sharing common design characteristics, components, modules, and manufacturing methods and technology. This in turn leads to dramatic reductions in new product introduction time, design and manufacturing staff, evaluation methods such as FMEA, as well as inventory, training, and manufacturing productivity; in short, lean design. There are similarities to the Modularity concept and GT (group technology), but goes far wider. Product platforms are found from calculators (e.g. Casio) to Cars (VW / Audi).

Cusumano and Nobeoka illustrate how the concept of platforms has developed. Although GM has been sharing "platforms" for decades, its 1993 models still had over 200 different steering columns and 44 power-steering pumps. But the impact of Chrysler's development of a recreational vehicle on the platform of an existing car, provided a huge spur. Cusumano and Nobeoka point out that today in the car industry there is intra-company, international, and inter-company alliance platform sharing. They warn, however, that although technology transfers of this type can be highly economical, cases are occurring where the transfer of old technology may be a disadvantage from a manufacturing viewpoint. Their research shows that sequential transfers (see the above section on New Product Organisation) can actually increase the development lead-time.

Two classic cases, cited by Meyer and Lehnerd, are Black and Decker tools and Hewlett Packard Ink Jet printers. In the 1970s, Black and Decker's product portfolio comprised scores of different motors, armatures, materials, and tooling, most of it simply evolving piecemeal one at a time. The company began their product platform strategy by bringing together design and manufacturing engineers to work in teams. They started, Pareto fashion, with the motor, and created a common core design with a single diameter but varying length, able to be adapted to power output from 60 to 650 watts. The range of motors now shared common manufacturing facilities, reduced changeover, and dramatically better quality. After motors, armatures and then drill bits were tackled. This led to reductions of 85% in operators, and 39% in cost. The cycle time for new product introduction was slashed, eventually enabling B&D to introduce new products at the rate of one per week. The extra investment needed for process technology was repaid within months. Lower costs were passed onto customers, and new markets created, resulting in a surge of demand and the decimation of competitors. Sadly, B&D have apparently slipped back to one-off thinking of late - a warning that continuing vigilance is necessary.

The Hewlett Packard printer story continues to evolve. Since 1980, HP has evolved from single colour black and white, to colour, to both, to portable, to scanner and copier included, whilst simultaneously continuously driving costs down at the one end and expanding features, print quality, speed, and versatility (for example into printer scanners, and printer faxes) at the other. Most share common components, technologies and manufacturing processes, as well as the lucrative printer cartridges. Further, the supplier base has been rationalised, and strong partnerships developed (see separate section).

Although not mentioned by Meyer and Lehnerd, it is significant that both B&D and HP are also leaders in manufacturing management. B&D were the oft-quoted prime examples of A class MRPII, then adopting JIT. HP, of course, has been perhaps the leading Western pioneer of JIT since the early 1980s. No doubt, these concepts helped one another.

Meyer and Lehnerd, identify five principles. These are

➔   Families should be identified, which share technology and are related to a market. (Note again similarity with GT which shares manufacturing process steps, but says nothing about markets). From this basic family feature-rich derivations are developed over time.

➜ Product design takes place alongside production design. (Product platforms are a strong argument in favour of the JIT "small machine" principle; too often, because of the existence of an expensive big machine, product designs are undertaken which seek to make use of the machine rather than giving first consideration to the customer.) Simultaneous design or concurrent design (a good Lean principle) should be used.

➜ Try to design for global standards, logistics, and component supply. (An example is the internationally adaptable power requirement used on HP printers).

➜ Try to capitalise on latent demands that a product platform can create. (VHS VCRs, and CDs are outstanding examples).

➜ Seek design elegance, not mere extension. (Java seems to be the reaction against bloated software packages with more and more features seldom used.)

The building blocks of product platforms, according to Meyer and Lehnerd are

➜ Market orientation, designers close to the customer (Lexus' design team living in California, Olympus designers working periodically in camera shops). And derivative products should be aimed at different market segments using the same basic platform; this should be part of the initial concept (example VW and Audi using the same platform but aimed at different segments, and through derivatives in engine size, and features, at different groups.)

➜ Using design building blocks - both internal and external (capitalising on the best product modules, rather than starting afresh).

➜ using the most appropriate manufacturing technologies, and

➜ Using the whole organisation - "total" innovation. Like TQM, product platforms require a cross-functional total approach along the whole chain.

Robertson and Ulrich say that platform planning involves an iterative tradeoff between product distinctiveness and the percentage of commonality. They advocate three interacting plans. The product plan maps out the timing of future variants. The differentiation plan maps "differentiating attributes" (i.e. characteristics that customers deem to be important) against product models, with the aim of seeking appropriate overlap. The commonality plan maps chunks (or modules or "corners") against models. Then a commonality plan is developed iteratively for each major chunk, which seeks to maximise the tradeoffs between commonality and differentiation for each component, keeping in mind development costs, tooling costs, and manufacturing costs.

Tabrizi and Walleigh say there are three best practices in relation to product platform development. The first is not just having a clear map of future products but using such maps to unite key development teams and using them to make the necessary decisions. The second is to have a platform strategy that locks out competitors, by not allowing them to fill gaps in a developing product platform line. The third is for platform developers to keep talking to customers, both present and future, about their changing needs.

Notice that the principles of Product Platforms are in line with the 5 principles of Lean Thinking: Begin by specifying value (of the product platform family) as defined by the ultimate customer. Womack and Jones talk about ignoring "existing assets and technologies", and working with "strong, dedicated product teams" when doing this. Then identify the value stream and remove waste (exactly what the product platform concept tries to do). Then make the value creating steps flow (the product platform concept uses cellular design and production). And pull according to customer demand. (Here we could be reminded of the JIT principle of "variety as late as possible" whereby variety is retained in the form of common subassemblies until actually ordered by customers - a concept made much easier by product platform module design). And lastly, strive for "perfection", (surely made easier by platform designs rather than one-off design).

Finally, product platform thinking is also totally compatible with the ideas of target costing, where derivatives are rolled out over time whilst capitalising on platform economies. All the derivatives form a stream of target costed products. And, as Robin Cooper has pointed out this is done through Value Engineering (see separate sections on these topics).

FURTHER READING:

Marc Meyer and Alvin Lehnerd, *The Power of Product Platforms,* Free Press, New York, 1997, ISBN 0-684-82580-5

Behnan Tabrizi and Rick Walleigh, "Defining Next Generation Products: An Inside Look", *Harvard Business Review,* Nov-Dec 1997, pp116-124

Michael Cusumano and Kentaro Nobeoka, *Thinking Beyond Lean,* The Free Press, New York, 1998, ISBN 0-684-84918-6

Carliss Baldwin and Kim Clark, "Managing in an Age of Modularity", *Harvard Business Review,* Sept-Oct 1997, pp 84-93

David Robertson and Karl Ulrich, "Planning for Product Platforms", *Sloan Management Review,* Summer 1998, pp19-31

FOUR FIELDS MAPPING

Four fields mapping (FFM) is a "new wave" project management system, appropriate for cross-functional management tasks such as concurrent engineering or business process reengineering. It is in widespread use for this purpose in Japan, and since the early 1990s has become a popular tool with leading US technology and innovation-based firms. It should be seen as sitting alongside QFD, concurrent engineering, and target costing (see separate sections). Perhaps the use of FFM goes some way towards explaining why, typically, Japanese car companies can bring a car to market in two-thirds of the time with two-thirds of the people.

FFM has many of the features of traditional critical path analysis or Gantt Charts, but with a few extra useful twists. The principal differences seems to be (a) that it is not concerned so much with the critical time path as with the successful completion of cross functional tasks or events together with tier milestones and standards, and (b) is specifically cross functional. Like critical path analysis, the principal benefit is in drawing up the map with the team and exploring alternatives, rather than in the calculation of the critical path. In good Japanese tradition, FFM does seem to cram much onto one page. An outline of a FFM is shown in the figure.

The four fields are:

➜   The Team Members or cross functional departments that are involved in the project

➜   The Phases (or major stages) of the project, each one of which has to have clear entry and exit criteria, which detail exactly what information is needed to begin a phase and what needs to have been accomplished for the phase to end.

➜   Phases are in turn broken down into Tasks. Each task should also have a clear entry and exit point or criteria that must be identified. A task may include a milestone, gateway or review at which point a decision must be made as to whether to continue or not. These are shown as diamonds on the FFM, and indicate all that must participate in the decision. To think through in advance the tasks leading to a "go-no go" decision, and who will participate in that decision, appears to be a major advantage of FFM over traditional critical path analysis. Of course, the logical sequence of tasks is linked together as in a critical path chart.

→ Standards are applied to major tasks and phases. This is a way of bringing quality into the project planning process. The type of standard sought is pre-specified at the concept stage in the FFM, and then the tasks fill in the actual specifications or information when the project commences. For example, a task may be concerned with designing a disk brake: the standards to be worked to include the disk size, calliper pressure, and material, and completing the task provides the actual specifications. Standards define the types of information that must be obtained or produced. These may be R&D requirements, engineering specifications, manufacturing standards, or delivery performance.

Notice that the figure may look like a Gantt chart but it is not. It simply shows who is involved, and the sequence of activities. Likewise, the review "lozenge" shows which functions are to be involved in the review process.

For each phase there should be a leader. This is in addition to the overall project leader, who is normally a figure of considerable influence in the company, certainly one who is not overawed by functional heads. When the FFM has been set up for a project, each function can work largely independently, knowing exactly what they are working towards in terms of standards, exit points, and decisions. The number of project meetings is reduced. Again, this is classic Japanese; put a large amount of effort up front into planning and co-ordinating, and then get on with it

There is software available for FFM. This software enables not only progress to be charted, but to add notes, information, standards, and responsibilities. It also allows the functions to work fairly independently, but having a common reporting base. However, to be carried away by the software would be to lose much of the advantage of FFM, which is really in team participation. Buying the software is not the miracle cure; in fact you do not need software at all - it is nice to have, not essential.

FURTHER READING:
Dan Dimancescu, *The Seamless Enterprise,* Harper Business, New York, 1992, Chapter 8, ISBN 0-88730-544-X

QUALITY FUNCTION DEPLOYMENT

Quality Function Deployment is a "meta" technique that has grown hugely in importance over the last decade and is now used in both product and service design. It is a meta technique because many other techniques described in this book can or should be used in undertaking QFD design or analysis. These other techniques include several of the "new tools", benchmarking, market surveys, the Kano model, the performance - importance matrix, and FMEA.

Customer needs are identified and systematically compared with the technical or operating characteristics of the product or service. The process brings out the relative importance of customer needs which, when set against the characteristics of the product leads to the identification of the most important or sensitive characteristics. These are the characteristics that need development or attention. Although the word "product" is used in the descriptions that follow, QFD is equally applicable in services. Technical characteristics then become the service characteristics.

Perhaps a chief advantage of QFD is that a multi-disciplinary team consisting of all concerned with the particular product carries it out. QFD acts as a forum for marketing, design, engineering, manufacturing, distribution and others to work together using a concurrent or simultaneous engineering approach. QFD is then the vehicle for these specialists to attack a problem together rather than by "throwing the design over the wall" to the next stage. QFD is therefore not only concerned with quality but with the simultaneous objectives of reducing overall development time, meeting customer requirements, reducing cost, and producing a product or service which fits together and works well the first time. The mechanics of QFD are not cast in stone, and can easily be adapted to local innovation.

The first QFD matrix is also referred to as the "house of quality". This is because of the way the matrices in QFD fit together to form a house-shaped diagram. A full QFD exercise may deploy several matrix diagrams, forming a sequence that gradually translates customer requirements into specific manufacturing steps and detailed manufacturing process requirements. For instance, a complete new car could be considered at the top level but subsequent exercises may be concerned with the engine, body shell, doors, instrumentation, brakes, and so on. Thereafter the detail would be deployed into manufacturing and production. But the most basic QFD exercise would use only one matrix diagram that seeks to take customer requirements and to translate them into specific technical requirements.

THE "HOUSE OF QUALITY" DIAGRAM

In the sections below the essential composition of the basic house of quality diagram is explained. Refer to the figure Quality Function Deployment opposite/overleaf.

CUSTOMER REQUIREMENTS

The usual starting point for QFD is the identification of customer needs and benefits. This is also referred to as "the voice of the customer" or "the whats". Customers may be present or future, internal or external, primary or secondary. All the conventional tools of marketing research are relevant, as well as techniques such as complaint analysis and focus groups. Customers may include owners, users, and maintainers, all of whom have separate requirements. Refer to the section on market research. After collection comes the problem of how to assemble the information before entering it into the rows. In this the "new tools" of affinity and tree diagrams have been found to be especially useful. This results in a hierarchy; on the primary level are the broad customer requirements, with the secondary requirements adding the detail.

QUALITY FUNCTION DEPLOYMENT (QFD)

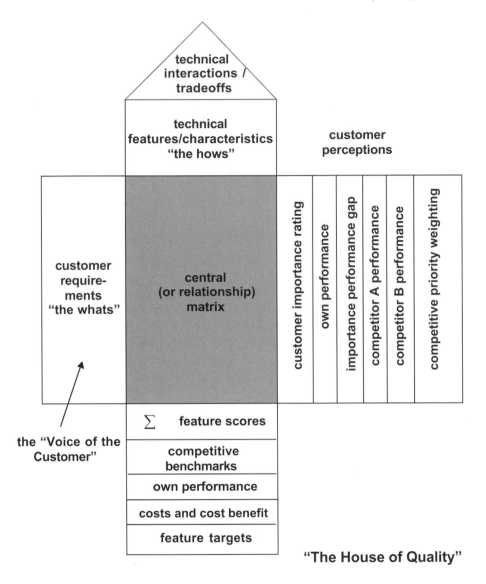

"The House of Quality"

Marketing would have responsibility for assembling much of the customer information, but the team puts it together. Marketing may begin by circulating the results of surveys and by a briefing. It is important to preserve the "voice of the customer", but the team may group like requirements using the affinity diagram. The team must not try to "second guess" or to assume that they know best what customers need.

RANKINGS OR RELATIVE IMPORTANCE OF CUSTOMER REQUIREMENTS

When the customer requirements are assembled onto the matrix on the left of the house diagram, weightings are added on the right to indicate the importance of each requirement. Market research or focus groups establish weightings or, failing these, the team may determine rankings by a technique such as "pairwise comparison". (In pairwise comparison, each requirement is compared with each other. The more important of the two requirements gains a point, and all scores are added up to determine final rankings.) The Kano model (see separate section) is very often used with QFD as an aid in determining appropriate weightings.

TECHNICAL CHARACTERISTICS AND ASSOCIATED RANKINGS

Customer requirements and weightings are displayed in rows. The technical characteristics (or "hows" or "technical responses") form the columns. These characteristics are the features that the organisation provides in the design to respond to the customer requirements (For a kettle this may include power used, strength of the materials, insulation, sealing, materials used, and noise.) Once again these could be assembled into groups to form a hierarchy, using the Tree Diagram. Here the team will rely on its own internal expertise. There are at least two ways to develop technical characteristics. One way is go via measures that respond to customer needs. For instance a customer need for a kettle may be "quick boil". The measure is "minutes to boil" and the technical response is the power of the heating element. Another is to go directly to functions, based on the team's experience or on current technology.

THE PLANNING MATRIX

To the right of the central matrix is found the planning matrix. This is a series of columns that evaluate the importance, satisfaction, and goal for each customer need. (See the figure). The first column shows importance to the customer of each need. Here a group of customers may be asked to evaluate the importance of each need on a 1 to 5 scale (1=not important, 5=vital, of highest importance). In the next column the current performance of each product or service need, is rated by the group of customers. The difference between the columns is the gap - a negative number indicates possible overprovision, a positive number indicates a shortfall. The reader will recognise that here the QFD process is duplicating the importance-performance matrix (see separate section), or the SERVQUAL gaps. The next few columns give the competitor's current performance on each customer need. The aim of this part of the exercise is to clearly identify the "SWOT" (strengths, weaknesses, opportunities, threats) of competitor products as against your own. For example, the kettle manufacturer may be well known for product sturdiness, but be weak on economy. If economy is highly ranked, this will point out an opportunity and, through the central matrix, show what technical characteristics can be used to make up this deficiency. The gap (if any) between own and competitors performance can then be determined. Since the QFD team now has detail on the gap for each need and of the importance of each need, they can then decide the desired goal for each customer need - normally expressed in the same units as the performance column. Deciding the goal for each need is an important task for the QFD team. These goals are the weights to be used in the relationship matrix. (Note: in some versions of QFD there are additional columns).

THE CENTRAL (OR RELATIONSHIP) MATRIX

The central matrix lies at the heart of the house of quality diagram. This is where customer needs are matched against each technical characteristic. The nature of the relationship is noted in the matrix by an appropriate symbol. The team can devise their own symbols; for instance, numbers may indicate the relative strength of the relationship or simply ticks may suffice. The strength of the relationship or impact is recorded in the matrix. These relationships may be nil, possibly linked, moderately linked or strongly linked. Corresponding weights (typically 0, 1, 3, 9) are assigned. Thereafter the scores for each technical characteristic are determined as in the "new tool" of Matrix Analysis (refer to the section in this book which details how a total score is determined for each characteristic). The team based on their experience and judgement carries out this matching exercise. The idea is to clearly identify all means by which the "whats" can be achieved by the "hows". It will also check if all "whats" can in fact be achieved (insufficient technical characteristics?), and if some technical characteristics are not apparently doing anything (redundancy?). A blank row indicates a customer requirement not met. A blank column indicates a redundant technical feature. In practice, matrix evaluation can be a very large task (a moderate size QFD matrix of 30 x 30 has 900 cells to be evaluated). The team may split the task between them.

MATRIX ANALYSIS for QFD

Example : Design of a Hamburger to Customer preferences

Begin with a Focus Group to determine Customer Requirements and relative weightings. Then :

Customer Requirements	Customer preference weighting	Features			
		Beef	Bun	Lettuce	
Seasoning	1	0 / 0	0 / 0	1 / 1	9 / 9
Flavour	3	27 / 9	0 / 0	0 / 0	9 / 3
Nutrition	3	27 / 9	9 / 3	0 / 0	0 / 0
Visual Appeal	5	45 / 9	5 / 1	5 / 1	5 / 1
Value for Money	5	45 / 9	5 / 1	0 / 0	5 / 1

	Beef	Bun	Lettuce	
Weighted scores	144	19	6	28
Benchmarks				
Relative Cost	6	2	1	1
Score / Cost	24	9.5	6	28

Conclusion : Concentrate attention on Beef and Ketchup

TECHNICAL MATRIX

Immediately below the relationship matrix appears one or more rows for rankings such as cost or technical difficulty or development time. The choice of these is dependent on the product. These will enable the team to judge the efficacy of various technical solutions. The prime row uses the customer weightings and central matrix to derive the relative technical characteristic rankings. A full example is given under Matrix Analysis in the New Tools section of this booklet.

Next, below the relationship matrix, comes one or more rows for competitive evaluation. Here, where possible, "hard" data is used to compare the actual physical or engineering characteristics of your product against those of competitors. In the kettle example these would include watts of electricity, mass, and thermal conductivity of the kettle walls. This is where benchmarking is done. By now the QFD team will know the critical technical characteristics, and these should be benchmarked against competitors (See the section on Benchmarking - especially competitive benchmarking). So to the right of the relationship matrix one can judge relative customer perceptions and below the relative technical performance.

The bottom row of the house, which is also the "bottom line" of the QFD process, is the target technical characteristics. These are expressed in physical terms and are decided upon after team discussion of the complete house contents, as described below. The target characteristics are, for some, the final output of the exercise, but many would agree that it is the whole process of information assembly, ranking, and team discussion that goes into QFD which is the real benefit, so that the real output is improved inter-functional understanding.

THE ROOF OF THE HOUSE

The roof of the house is the technical interaction matrix. The diagonal format allows each technical characteristic to be viewed against each other one. This simply reflects any technical tradeoffs that may exist. For example with the kettle two technical characteristics may be insulation ability and water capacity. These have a negative relationship; increasing the insulation decreases the capacity. These interactions are made explicit, using the technical knowledge and experience of the team. Some cells may highlight challenging technical issues - for instance thin insulation in a kettle, which may be the subject of R&D work leading to competitive advantage. The roof is therefore useful to highlight areas in which R&D work could best be focused.

USING THE HOUSE AS A DECISION TOOL

The central matrix shows what the required technical characteristics are that will need design attention. The costs of these can be seen with reference to the base rows. This may have the effect of shifting priorities if costs are important. Then the technical tradeoffs are examined. Often there will be more than one technical way to impact a particular customer requirement, and this is clear from rows in the matrix. It may also be that one technical alternative has a negative influence on another customer requirement. This is found out by using the roof matrix. Eventually, through a process of team discussion, a team consensus will emerge. This may take some time, but experience shows that time and cost is repaid many times over as the actual design, engineering and manufacturing steps proceed.

The bottom line is now the target values of technical characteristics. This set can now go into the next house diagram. This time the target technical characteristics become the "customer requirements" or "whats", and the new vertical columns (or "hows") are, perhaps, the technologies, the assemblies, the materials, or the layouts. And so the process "deploys" until the team feels that sufficient detail has been considered to cover all co-ordination considerations in the process of bringing the product to market.

Note: QFD may be used in several stages in order to "deploy" customer requirements all the way to the final manufacturing or procedural stages. Here the outcome of one QFD matrix (e.g. the technical specifications) becomes the input into the next matrix that may aim to look at process specifications to make the product.

ASSEMBLING THE TEAM

A QFD team should have up to a dozen members with representation from all sections concerned with the development and launch of the product. Team composition may vary depending on whether new products or the improvement of existing products is under consideration. The important thing is that there is representation from all relevant sections and disciplines. There may well be a case for bringing in outsiders to stimulate the creative process and to ask the "silly" questions. Team members must have the support of their section heads. These section heads may feel it necessary to form a steering group. QFD teams are not usually full time, but must be given sufficient time priority to avoid time clashes. The team leader may be full time for an important QFD. The essential characteristics are team leadership skills rather than a particular branch of knowledge.

RELATIONSHIP WITH OTHER TECHNIQUES

As mentioned. QFD is a "meta" technique in that several other techniques can be fitted in with it. For example, value management may be used to explore some of the technical alternatives, costs and tradeoffs in greater detail. Taguchi analysis is commonly used with QFD because it is ideally suited to examining the most sensitive engineering characteristics so as to produce a robust design. Failure mode and effect analysis (FMEA) can be used to examine consequences of failure, and so to throw more light on the technical interactions matrix. And mention has already been made of the use of various "New Tools". In the way the QFD team carries out its work, weights alternatives, generates alternatives, groups characteristics, and so on, there are many possibilities. QFD only provides the broad concept. There is much opportunity for adaptation and innovation.

FURTHER READING:

Ronald G. Day, *Quality Function Deployment,* ASQC Quality Press, Milwaukee, WI, 1994
Lou Cohen, *Quality Function Deployment: How to make QFD work for you,* Addison Wesley, Reading MA, 1995
John Terninko, *Step by Step QFD,* Second Edition, St Lucie Press, Boca Raton FL, 1997, ISBN 1-57444-110-8

TRIZ

TRIZ is a family of techniques, developed originally in Russia, for product invention and creativity. It is superb for innovative product design, and for production process problem solving. TRIZ is a Russian acronym for the theory of inventive problem solving. In 1948, the originator of TRIZ, Genrich Altshuller, suggested his ideas on improving inventive work to Stalin (a big mistake!), and was imprisoned in Siberia until 1954. His ideas once again fell into disfavour and only emerged with perestroyka. The first TRIZ ideas reached the U.S. in the mid 1980s.

The fundamental belief of TRIZ is that invention can be taught. All (?) inventions can be reduced to a set of rules or principles. There may be a flash of genius, but the principles, relying on physics, engineering, and knowledge of materials can be taught. Here, only a brief overview or flavour of some of the 40 principles can be attempted. Even so, some will be immediately useful. TRIZ is bound to, and deserves to, become better known. We hope this will be a stimulant to you to acquire some TRIZ publications. Some of the inventive principles are:

Do it inversely (Inversion)
How do you get liquor into a chocolate sweet > freeze the liquor!
Do it in advance (Prior Action)
How do you reduce changeover time > do as much work as possible beforehand.
"Matreshka" (Nesting) or Russian dolls (where one is found inside another) suggests placing one device inside another - such as a motor inside a pipe for drain clearing. Self-cleaning glass. Combining printer, fax, scanner, copier, answer machine into one unit.
Separate conflicting requirements in time or space
A farm vehicle has to be powerful and economical, but not always at the same time > so arrange to disengage 4 the four wheel drive when not required.
Incorporating different objects into one system
Here, Altschuller describes the evolution of ships, by incorporation of additional features whilst dropping others: oars > oars + sail > sail + paddle > sail + motor > motor > turbine. Evolution is part of invention. Think Formula 1.
Replace special terms with ordinary words
This allows you to think differently and creatively: EDI > linked communications (multi stage down the supply chain?). MRP > ordering materials when required. (automatic reordering when reorder point is reached by weight?). SPC > tracking the machine, not inspecting the product (a sensor to detect 3 sigma variation?)
"Operator STC" (Size, Time, Cost)

Questions for an inventor to consider are what will happen if size is increased or decreased? What will happen if time is increased or decreased? And what if cost is zero or infinite? Consider a map book that is difficult to handle in a car: now there are miniature maps available. How to convey goods much faster in a factory: use the hovercraft principle? Slower, but steadier: float it? If presses had infinite cost, how could metal be formed: injection? If painting had infinite cost: paint mixed with plaster? Or steel which rusts to a weatherproof finish?)

A partial list of some of the 40 inventive problems includes: partial or overdone action (if you can't solve the whole problem, solve just a part to simplify it), moving to a new dimension (use multi layers, turn it on its side, move it along a plane, etc.) self-service (make the product service itself, make use of wasted energy), changing the colour (or make it transparent, use a coloured additive), mechanical vibration (use its vibrations or oscillations, use a mechanical or ultrasound vibrator), hydraulic or pneumatic assembly (replace solids with gas or liquid, join parts hydraulically), porous material (make the part porous, or fill the pores in advance), thermal expansion (use these properties, change to more than one material with different coefficients of expansion), copying (instead of using the object use a copy or a projection of it), thin membranes (use flexible membranes, insulate or isolate using membranes), regenerating parts (recycle), use a composite material. This is a powerful list - just reading them can stimulate ideas.

Altschuller emphasises thinking in terms of the "ideal machine" or ideal solution as a first step to problem solving. You have a hot conservatory? It should open by itself when the temperature rises! So now think of devices that will achieve this: bimetallic expansion strips, expanding gas balloons, a solar powered fan.

A general methodology comprises three steps: First, determine why the problem exists. Second, "state the contradiction". Third, "imagine the ideal solution", or imagine yourself as a magician who can create anything. For example, consider the problem of moving a steel beam. Why is it a problem? Because it cannot roll. The contradiction is that the shape prevents it from rolling. So, ideally, it should roll. How? By placing semi-circular inserts on each side along the beam.

Finally, invention requires practice and method. Like golfer Gary Player who said the more he practised the better his luck seemed to get, Altschuller suggests starting young and keeping one's mind in shape with practice problems. Also keeping a database of ideas gleaned from a variety of publications. (Refer also to the section on Learning).

Many TRIZ ideas require some technical knowledge, or at least technical aptitude. Therefore it will not work well with every group. However, it is most useful for designers, technical problem solvers, persons involved with QFD, and for implementation of lean manufacturing (particularly the technical issues).

FURTHER READING:

 G. Altschuller, *And Suddenly the Inventor Appeared,* Technical Innovation Centre, Inc., Worcester MA, 1996, ISBN 0-9640740-2-8

John Terninko, Alla Zusman, Boris Zlotin, *Systematic Innovation: An Introduction to TRIZ,* St. Lucie Press, Boca Raton, FL, 1998, ISBN 1-57444-111-6

Stan Kaplan, *An Introduction to TRIZ,* Ideation International, Southfield MI, 1996

CONCEPT SCREENING

Concept screening is a simple but powerful tool used not only to home in on the best concept or alternative, but also to improve it. The late Stuart Pugh's method is widely used for QFD, but also with lean implementation and layout, product design and development, and project selection.

Concept screening uses a matrix approach. See the figure. A team, preferably multidisciplinary or from a "diagonal slice" should do the work. Competing concepts are listed in the columns. It is often useful to include a sketch in each column. Concept screening works best when there are less than about 10 competing concepts, so if the number is greater than this use multi voting to select the top 10. Multi voting simply gives 5 votes to each participant who may allocate them between the concepts as he or she pleases.

The selection criteria are listed in the rows, and are chosen based on customer needs and organisation needs. The latter may include cash flow, manufacturability, and marketing compatibility. Generally there would be a maximum of around 20 selection criteria. One important consideration, however, is that the selection criteria (at this stage) should exclude relatively unimportant factors.

Then, following team discussion, one of the concepts is selected as the benchmark or baseline. This may be a competitors product or an industry standard.

Thereafter, each concept is evaluated against the baseline concept, for each criteria, simply using a + sign where better than, - (negative sign) where worse than, and 0 where approximately the same. The team should seek consensus on these evaluations. Many will be clear, but where there is direct quantitative information available this should be used directly. For instance, in evaluating competing factory layouts one of the criteria may be flow length. The lengths in each concept should be measured. Other examples are the number of parts where inventory or assembly time is one of the criteria.

Following the rating exercise, the scores for each concept are added up. A + counts +1, a - (negative) counts -1, and a zero counts zero. This establishes the rank order.

Before discarding any concept, ways should first be sought of improving it. Look at the negatives and ask if features affecting these criteria can be incorporated. (The TRIZ concept may be useful

Pugh's Concept Screening Technique

Selection Criteria	Concept			
	Layout 1	**Layout 2**	**Layout 3**	**Layout 4**
Speed	0	- 1	0	+ 1
Cost	0	+ 1	- 1	+ 1
Reliability	0	+ 1	+ 1	0
Flow Length	0	- 1	0	+ 1
Flexibility	0	- 1	+ 1	- 1
Quality	0	- 1	0	+ 1
Score	0	- 2	+ 1	+ 3

Conclusion : Layout 4 looks most promising, but can the
Reliability features from Layout 2 or 3 be incorporated ?
Flexibility features from Layout 3 be incorporated ?

here - see separate section). Another option may be to create a hybrid design, combining the best features from two or more options. Such re-evaluations may require the concept screening session to be delayed to allow greater investigation or redesign.

Finally the team reassembles and makes the final selection, often involving a repeat of the scoring process and now incorporating less important criteria. Again, consensus should be sought, and the outcome should make sense to all. If anyone is uncomfortable with the outcome it may be that one or more selection criteria is redundant or missing. This may involve yet another round of evaluation. The outcome is not the best answer, but a short list of the most promising options - for further investigation.

FURTHER READING:
Stuart Pugh, *Total Design,* Addison Wesley, Reading MA, 1990, ISBN 0-201-41639-5
Stuart Pugh, *Creating Innovative Products Using Total Design,* Addison Wesley, Reading MA, ISBN 0-201-634-85-6

ANALYSIS AND MAPPING

→ Takt Time
→ System Dynamics, Systems Thinking, and Learning
→ Product Contribution Analysis
→ The Muda Map
→ Storyboarding and Brown Paper Exercise
→ Value Stream Mapping
→ Overall Lead Time Mapping
→ Order Mapping
→ Customer Mapping
→ "Learning to See" Mapping
→ Process Activity Mapping
→ Product Variety Funnel
→ Quality Filter Mapping
→ Demand Amplification Mapping
→ Push Pull Mapping
→ Physical Structure Mapping
→ Capacity Mapping
→ Cost Time Profile
→ Business Process Mapping
→ Time Charting and Analysis
→ Soft Systems Methodology
→ Self Audits

TAKT TIME

Takt time is the fundamental concept to do with the regular, uniform rate of progression of products through all stages from raw material to customer. As such it is important in planning, in cell balancing, and in facility design. It should also be a consideration along a complete supply chain. "Sell daily? make daily!" is the underlying idea. Takt time is the drumbeat cycle of the rate of flow of products. It is the "metronome" (from the German origins of the word). Understanding takt time is fundamental to analysis and mapping of Lean Operations, and hence heads this section.

Takt time is most simply the average rate at which customers buy products and hence the rate at which products should be manufactured. It is expressed in time units: one every so many minutes or so many minutes between completions.

But perhaps this is too simple. Takt time is the available weekly work time, taking into account the shifts worked and making allowances for planned stoppages (for planned maintenance, team briefings, breaks) divided by the anticipated average weekly sales rate (including spare parts) plus any extras such as test parts and (we hope not) anticipated scrap.

Some companies allow for changeover times in calculating the available weekly work time. This is not really good practice because the takt drumbeat must be maintained throughout the plant, including changeovers. However provided there are good standards for changeover and that batch sizes are calculated keeping in mind the customer's rate of demand, it may be tolerable. Also, some companies make allowances for breakdowns and OEE in available time. This is not so reasonable because this may build in bad practice.

Notice that this takt time formula is given in relation to a week. A day will often be too short. A month will often be too long, although at Toyota a takt time can remain in force for several months. Takt time should be changeable from week to week or month to month, depending on the environment. This means that lines may have to be rebalanced week by week, which in turn means that operators should be involved in the task of rebalancing and know the concept of takt time. Note that takt time is not cycle time, which is the time required to complete a series of operations. Cycle time should be allocated so as to be less than or equal to takt time. (See the section on Cell Design and Flexible Manpower Lines.)

For machines and processes, working at the takt time may mean <u>slowing down</u>. Strangely and counter-intuitively, slowing down to achieve synchronisation may lead to a reduction in lead-time. This is because queues build up after machines that run faster than the takt time. This simple realisation, to try to get all machines in a plant running at the constant takt time, can have dramatic results. It changes the job shop into a pseudo assembly line.

Takt time should drive the whole thinking of the plant and the supply chain. In a plant it is the drumbeat. Consideration needs to be given to the number of parts per product sold. Thus if there are four wheels per trolley sold, and wheels are all made on the same machine, the wheel machine needs to have a takt time of approximately one quarter that of the main assembly line. (Approximately because there may be setups involved and there may be a special demands for additional spare wheels). So takt times in a plant leads to overall synchronisation. That is the whole idea. Even more challenging is producing at this rate. Often a machine is capable of producing in a much shorter cycle that the takt time. If so, the manager, or preferably the operators, need to think how it will all work; can an operator tend several machines so that the rate of output is slowed to match the takt time? Or perhaps move between machines after making a small batch? In any case try to meet the rate every hour or every half-day or every day; the more frequently the better Remember the idea is to maintain flow.

Takt time should be used for monitoring and control, to encourage linear production. Knowing the takt time establishes the number of items that should be completed at any time of the day. In a supply chain, each organisation should calculate (weekly?) its own takt time based upon the overall end-product sales rate. This means, of course, that the end product sales rate should be known right along the chain. If takt time is known right along a supply chain, then the disastrous "bullwhip" effects can be avoided.

In a plant, it may be that a machine makes parts going into several products each week, with changeover times between products. In this case, begin with available net time after planned stoppages. Classify products into runners, repeaters and strangers. (See the separate section on this. Runners, of course, have their own dedicated facilities.) Then see if it is possible with current changeover times to make every product (runners and strangers) every week. <u>If yes,</u> arrange the repeaters in descending order and calculate how many can be run twice per week, then three times and so on until all available time has been taken up. You may decide not to run each product more than once per week. Deducting the total changeover time gives the net actual working time. Now calculate takt time for each product by dividing the times by the total product requirements. <u>If no,</u> try to run the big repeaters as frequently as possible.

System Dynamics, Systems Thinking, and Learning

Professor Jay Forrester started system Dynamics, also known as Industrial Dynamics, at MIT in the 1950's. It is a modelling technique for understanding complex systems, especially those where feedback plays an important role (and, some contend, all real world systems are of this type.) As a concept, its popularity seems to have followed some cycles, not unlike the non-linear behaviour of the systems that it seeks to understand and model. System dynamics received a boost in the early 1970s with the publication of the Club of Rome's report on "Limits to Growth" which used system dynamics to understand the interaction of the developing growth of population and pollution, the decline in natural resources, standard of living/quality of life, a shortage of food and arable land. The fact that the forecasts of impending doom did not materialise (at least not in the timescale predicted), led to a credibility gap blamed unfairly on the technique.

Subsequently, System Dynamics received a huge boost with the publication of Peter Senge's book "The Fifth Discipline", and later "The Fifth Discipline Fieldbook". Today, System Dynamics is taught at leading Business Schools and used by some companies as a way of understanding their complex operating environment, rather than attempting to make accurate forecasts. It is the "counter-intuitive" nature of some of behaviours that are modelled, which makes it a particularly fascinating and useful technique. System Dynamics may be used in two ways : either by building formal computer models (using a modelling language such as Microworld, or iThink), or by simply drawing out the feedback loops and discussing them through. (The Fifth Discipline, according to Senge, is Systems Thinking).

In any system there are two types of feedback loop at work : A positive feedback (or reinforcing) loop leading to unlimited exponential growth (such as money in a building society generating interest, hence more capital, hence more interest, forever), and a negative, or goal seeking feedback loop (such as a thermostat homing in on the target temperature). No real world system, it is argued, goes on growing in an unlimited way. A successful new product, for instance, may grow due to feedback of satisfied customers telling their friends. But, sooner or later, problems such as longer lead times, shortages, or less motivated staff, develop which eventually feeds back to dissatisfied customers who no longer recommend the product to their friends. Possible feedback loops are shown in the figure. Putting these loops together is called causal loop diagramming.

In the diagram a positive sign next to arrowheads indicates that the factor at the head of the arrow moves in the same direction as the factor at the tail. A negative sign indicates that the factors move in opposite directions. In any complete loop, an even (or zero) number of negative signs indicates a positive (growth) loop, an odd number of negative signs indicates a negative (goal seeking) loop.

System dynamics is a branch of wider Systems Thinking. A system is a set of entities together with the relationships between them. The essence of systems thinking is that it "seeks not to be reductionist" (a phrase from Peter Checkland). This means regarding the problem as a whole, rather than trying to break it down into constituent parts. (The opposite of this book!). The opposite of systems thinking is linear, cause and effect thinking. System dynamics teaches that there is hardly ever one answer to a problem or question. Instead, there are effective and less effective strategies. But it also teaches that there may be unexpected, or counterintuitive consequences.

A flow analogy is often used with system dynamics. There are "levels" and "rates". Think of the level in a water tank (or of the level of customer satisfaction). This level determines the rate of flow, perhaps in relation to a target value (the full tank, or a level of customer dissatisfaction that effectively shuts off further flow). Lags may be built into these feedback loops. In some feedback loops there may be several stages. The number of customers in a restaurant might lead to a decrease in waiter to customer ratio leading to delay leading to dissatisfaction leading to less positive recommendations leading back to the number of customers. A level, or index, may depend on several other components or levels, often in relation to some standards. For instance, the "quality" of restaurant service may depend upon the perceived level of the "RATER" dimensions of reliability (accuracy of order taking and bill), assurance (or knowledge of the waiter), tangibles (waiter and table neatness), empathy (or rapport with customers), and responsiveness (willingness to assist).

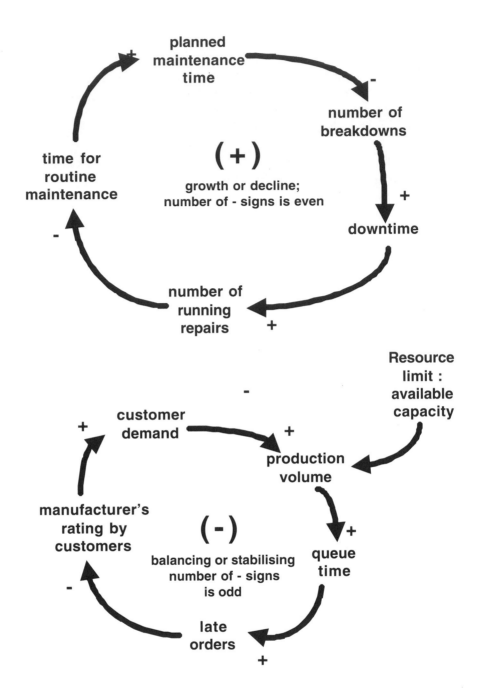

These factors may be added or multiplied to give the current level. And there may be delay for a change in level to work itself through. (For more on SERVQUAL see *The Quality 60*)

To begin constructing a System Dynamics model begin by selecting a problem and writing out the problem statement. Do this in a team, if possible. Then identify the key variables or levels. Now map the links between the variables with arrows. Label the head of the arrow with a + if both variables move in the same direction (more capital more interest) and with a - sign if the variables move in opposite directions (more customers, less time per waiter). Map in stages, one step at a time; don't leapfrog (example more customers, less service). Now identify whether the complete loops are positive or negative (a positive feedback loop has an even number of - signs, including nil or all + signs). Formulate hypotheses on the behaviour of the system. Now test, discuss, or collect evidence on, the system behaviour and on each loop. It's fun, and your understanding of systems that you find yourself in will grow apace.

LEARNING

Learning is inherent in Systems Thinking because real systems are complex and understanding must grow. Learning should ideally be institutionalised. It has been said that at IBM (but no doubt true for others) 90% of "new" things that are done have already been done. The problem is how to capture this experience. Today, with lean organisations, it is ever more important not to lose this experience.

Think of learning in terms of football. A Premier League team after each match spends time reviewing and evaluating performance, asking questions, seeking weaknesses, and then building in the tentative answers into the next match. This is like the Deming cycle. What a Premier League team does not do is just turn up for the next match. In business, learning means setting aside a short time at the end of meetings to review how it went and to seek and record better ways for next time. Similarly with new product launches, new ventures, projects, implementations, and the like. In this, system dynamics causal loop diagrams can be useful to show beliefs and assumptions on the workings of the meeting, project, or launch.

As an example, Boeing established a learning team to discuss and record why the development of the 737 and 747 had experienced many problems, whereas the 707 and 727 had far fewer problems. Hundreds of recommendations and suggestions were collected. Members of the learning team were asked to join the 757 and 767 projects that turned out to be the most error free aircraft ever made by the company.

After Action Reviews (AARs) is the name given by the U.S. Army to institutionalise learning. It's a simple notion. Four questions are asked at the end of every project, exercise (or war?) : They are

> What was supposed to happen ?
> What actually happened ?
> Why were there differences ?
> What can we learn or do differently next time ?

The key to AARs is not only to record the knowledge, but also to transmit it to all relevant parties. This may involve a range of solutions from just simple written communication to parties considered relevant, to formal information systems.

As an example, Joy Manufacturing (an early pioneer of value engineering) in the 1980s set up a world-wide system to communicate all advances as a result of VE exercises to their plants around the world. Today similar and much more advanced information systems communicate the results of AARs to relevant parties at BP, Motorola, and General Electric. At Toyota simple checklists are kept, updated, and circulated.

A variation on this are personal web pages that are encouraged to be published on the company intranet at BP. Such web pages contain the skills, interests, achievements, current projects, and thoughts and ideas of staff, and are amenable to search by web search engines. Note that Learning is not confined to new products. Relevant and valuable learning takes place in projects, on the shop floor, at the point of encounter with customers, and with suppliers, to name but a few. It should form a part of every continuous improvement programme, and as such, should be an integral part of the Lean Enterprise.

Another innovation is the use of "The Green Book" at NatWest Markets. This is a frequently updated cross reference document, issued to all employees, so that they can locate the right person to ask for any item of information that they need. It is a form of knowledge database of topics and people, rather than information.

Dussauge and Garrette tell a story about learning at GM and Toyota. The NUMMI joint venture in California was deliberately set up to allow GM to lean Japanese manufacturing techniques and for Toyota to gain knowledge about the American market. GM executives spent three year terms at NUMMI, attempting to learn it all, before returning to their own divisions. The impact on learning was minimal however because those executives were too thinly spread amongst the huge, and generally unsupportive, GM empire. Toyota executives, by contrast, focused only on American labour and supply methods. They gained an in-depth knowledge of these areas and made a large impact on those relevant sections at Toyota.

FURTHER READING:
Peter Senge, Charlotte Roberts, Richard Ross, Bryan Smith, Art Kleiner, *The Fifth Discipline Fieldbook,* Nicholas Brealey, London, 1994 ISBN 1-85788-060-9
Alan Waring, *Practical Systems Thinking,* Thompson Business Press, London, ISBN 0-412-71750-6
David Garvin, *Building a Learning Organization,* Harvard Business Review, July/Aug 1993
Steven Prokesch, "Unleashing the Power of Learning : An Interview with British Petrolium's John Browne", *Harvard Business Review,* Sept-Oct 1997, pp 147-158
Peter Dussage and Bernard Garrette, *Cooperative Strategy,* Wiley, New York, 1999
Thomas Davenport and Laurence Prusak, *Working Knowledge: How Organisations Manage What They Know,* Harvard Business School Press, 1998

PRODUCT CONTRIBUTION ANALYSIS

Contribution analysis is an evaluation technique that looks at the relative contribution of a company's product range. Products are arranged, Pareto fashion, in a family of graphs showing unit product contribution, total contribution, and contribution per bottleneck minute. It is used to rationalise the product portfolio or to help keep the portfolio on track. Specifically, the technique helps identify those products that should be dropped from the portfolio and those product types that should be developed. The technique should be applied at the start of every lean manufacturing project, and should be revisited at regular intervals, say once per year.

To set up the graph:

→ Arrange the full list of the company's products in ascending order of unit product contribution (that is, selling price - direct costs, for one unit of the product).

→ Accumulate the total unit contribution. If there are products with negative contributions, ignore these.

→ Calculate the percentage unit contribution of each product. (unit product contribution x 100 / total unit contribution)

→ Calculate the cumulative percentage by product

→ Draw out the resulting graph, Pareto style. That is, plot the cumulative unit contribution on the vertical axis, against the products ranked from highest contribution to lowest on the horizontal axis, as shown). Note that at the right hand side the graph may slope downwards indicating negative contributions.

→ Repeat steps 1 to 5, but this time use total contribution (that is, unit contribution x annual volume).

→ Identify the bottleneck resource, or near bottleneck resources, in the plant. You may be helped on this if you have done the Capacity Profile Map. If you have not, merely use "common knowledge" as to which are the bottleneck resources.

→ For each bottleneck resource, or for the main bottleneck resource only, obtain the unit run time for each product on that bottleneck. If a product does not go through the bottleneck, ignore that product. Now divide the unit contribution for each product by the run time on the bottleneck.

→ Repeat steps 1 to 5, using unit contribution per bottleneck minute.

Almost invariably you will find a long tail, and sometimes a downward sloping tail, on each of the graphs. The unit contribution graph is most useful to identify products making negative contributions. The priority should be to cease manufacturing the right-most products on the graph.

The contribution per bottleneck minute graph is the most powerful and relevant of the family of graphs. Clearly, products that make small or negative contribution, and which tie up bottleneck resources should be prime candidates for rationalisation. On the other hand products making even a small contribution, but which do not involve bottleneck resources are worth keeping.

The discussion as to the future product line will be aided by looking at the contribution per bottleneck minute graph, together with the total contribution graph. Of course, there may be products that fall into the "cut" category, but which cannot be removed because they form a family to one customer who takes several favourable products. In this case, some of the options may be to renegotiate the contract, to change the product routing, to change the design, or to ensure that a higher price is asked for next time around.

Contribution Analysis

THE MUDA MAP

To get an initial impression of how people in an organisation regard waste or muda, it is useful to do an "importance performance" opinion survey.

First, give out a short description of the 7 wastes. Make sure everyone understands the various types of waste. Then ask about the importance of each of the wastes to current company objectives. This can be done in several ways.

The Lean Enterprise Research Centre at Cardiff asks people to distribute 35 points amongst the 7 wastes. A maximum score of 10 may be allocated to any waste, and a minimum of zero. Thus one cannot simply choose one of the wastes. Another method is to use pairwise ranking : ask people to rate the importance of each waste against each other waste. For example, do you think overproduction or with excessive transport is more important? Allocate a score of +1 to the waste indicated as most important. Allocate zero if both are considered equal. Do this between each pair of factors (for 7 wastes there are 21 comparisons to be made). Don't debate: just take the first reaction. Then simply add up the scores. This is a bit more time consuming but does force the person being surveyed to make specific comparisons. In any event you end up with the wastes given scores on current importance.

Now ask about current performance on each of the wastes in the company or cell. This is of course a different question to importance. Rate each waste on a 1 to 5 scale, 1 being very poor and 5 being excellent performance.

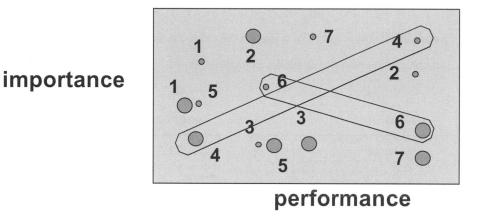

Then assemble the results on a two dimensional chart as shown. It is useful to do this exercise with different groups : operators, managers, and planners. Where the priorities lie is seldom seen in the same way. This gives an insight as to where to begin your analysis, and the difficulties to be overcome during implementation. Cardiff's Lean Enterprise Research Centre uses this as an entry point into further mapping.

Of course high priority should be given to areas of low performance but high importance, and low priority to areas of high performance but low importance.

STORYBOARDING AND BROWN PAPER EXERCISE

A **Storyboard** is simply the graphic *series* of panels on which is displayed the history of significant changes or proposals. This often relates to a particular problem faced by a team, and is displayed at the worksite ("at Gemba"). The point is that it is a series of graphics, not an isolated one, which together tell the story. Thus, a few charts put up on the notice board on the shop floor cannot be considered a storyboard.

Forsha makes the point that there are two approaches to problem solving: the traditional series of orderly steps (such as Deming' s PDCA cycle) or the Storyboard, which, according to Forsha, is more motivational and more fun. There is, however, no reason why both cannot be used together. Since it is displayed at the workplace, everyone can see progress and it is a constant reminder of past analysis and future prospects.

A typical storyboard will show most or all of the "7 Tools" of Quality (Process Chart, Pareto, Fishbone, Run Diagram, Histogram / Measles, Correlation / Stratification, Control Charts, and Check Sheets). Please refer to *The Quality 60* for a full description of these tools. Very often, financial figures on savings will also be shown.

In addition to the 7 tools, a storyboard should display the objective of the project and the names of the participants. There are a number of variations.

The **Ford Visualisation,** includes the following panels :

➜ A trend chart, showing target and actual performance against time

➜ A Pareto analysis showing the current top few problems

➜ A Histogram graphing the Pareto analysis

➜ An Action Plan, with a brief description of each task and who is responsible

➜ An Implementation record of actions taken, with dates and savings

➜ All this is shown on one chart. An example is shown.

Trend Chart

Actual

Target

Minutes

Action Plan

Description of Action	Resp.	Target	Progress
rearrange tool location	Paul	Week 5	90% done
tool redesign	Dave	Week 9	nil

Pareto

Stage	Quantity	%
1	30 min	15
2	85 min	42
3	10 min	5
4	25 min	13
5	8 min	4
6	42 min	21

Implementation Record

Action / Date	Impact / Date
setup trolley put in use. 11 Feb	saving of 10 mins in transport time

A variation, or addition, shows charts for Cost, Quality, Delivery, People, and Safety all relating to a particular project.

Radar charts and photographs are also useful. See our book *The Quality 60* (under Data Display) for various examples.

At Toyota the attitude is that it is preferable to have hand-drawn charts done by the operators, rather than neat computer-produced charts made in an office by a graphic package.

A **Brown paper Chart** is a variation. This typically shows an outline process chart on which is written various information. It is called "brownpaper" because typically such charts are quite long (perhaps 3 or 4 metres) and brownpaper is the easiest, cheapest material to use. On the chart, "Post Its" of different colours are often used to indicate status (perhaps green done, red to do, blue in progress). Contributed ideas are written on the chart. There may be supplementary graphs or charts, or photos relating to a particular process. The point is that the whole project is on display on one sheet of large paper. It serves as a constant reminder. It is also a focus point for the team to gather round to discuss progress. Such charts are used by operators, but are also a favourite of consultants. Once again utility rather than neatness is best. An example of a brownpaper chart is shown below, taken from an automotive metal pressing company.

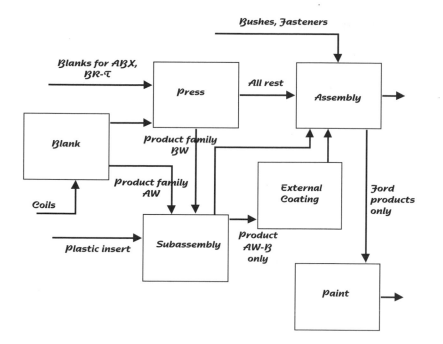

FURTHER READING:

Harry Forsha, *Show Me : The Complete Guide to Storyboarding and Problem Solving,* ASQC
Quality Press, Milwaukee WI, 1995, ISBN 0-87389-255-0
John Bicheno, *The Quality 60,* PICSIE Books, Buckingham, 1997

VALUE STREAM MAPPING INTRODUCTION

Peter Hines and Nick Rich of Cardiff Business School have brought together a set of seven mapping tools, some old and some new, which they have found to be most useful in the preliminary analysis of supply chains. Since Hines and Rich proposed their set considerable experience in mapping has been gained leading the author of this book to modify the original set. This section builds on the original Hines and Rich work, and also adds a few more tools. The tools are presented in more or less the order in which they should be undertaken.

GENERAL REFERENCE:

Peter Hines and Nick Rich, The Seven Value Stream Mapping Tools", *Int. Jnl. of Operations and Production Management,* Vol 17 No 1, 1997, pp 47-64
And for examples of applications see
Dan Dimancescu, Peter Hines and Nick Rich, The Lean Enterprise, AmaCom, New York, 1997, ISBN 0-8144-0365-4, and
A series of articles in *Logistics Focus* between January 1999 and September 1999, by David Taylor, John Bicheno, David Brunt, Nick Rich, and Peter Hines, and
Matthias Holweg, *Supply Chain Scheduling and the Automotive Steel Supply Chain,* MSc Thesis, University of Buckingham, 1998

OVERALL LEAD TIME MAPPING

The aim of the Lead Time Map is simply to track, quantify and prioritise the various elements of total lead time. For a time-based competitor, it should be one of the first, if not the first, map to draw. The idea is to draw a Pareto of where time is being spent or lost. Although it is important to know the breakdown of total lead time it is not necessary to spend much time on this map, and as such this map gives a high "bang for buck" ratio.

The elements of overall lead time are:

➔ Order entry time: Paperwork. The time from receipt of order to entry into the manufacturing and planning system.

➔ Configuration time: The time from entry into the system to completion of the configuration. In assemble to order or make to order this could involve design or CAD time and configuration checks. This time will probably be zero in make to stock environments, and may be zero or near zero in repetitive operations.

➔ Procurement time: The time taken to procure materials and components, to kit (if done) and to bring the materials from the store to the point of use. In repetitive operations some elements of procurement time could be regarded as zero where they are done routinely or in parallel with order entry time or configuration time.

➔ Non-specific manufacturing time. The time taken for "variety as late as possible" manufacturing stages, where components or subassemblies are not specific to a final product or order. Note that this time element may overlap or be done in parallel with order entry time and configuration time.

➔ Order-specific manufacturing time. The time taken in those manufacturing stages which are order- or customer-specific. This time may be zero in make-to-stock.

➔ Post production move and store time. The time from completion of manufacture to the start of delivery. This time may include final packaging.

➔ Delivery time. This may include final configuration in the case of products that are bundled to order.

The resulting time line may be a straight line, or may have overlapping sections. Where there are overlapping sections, take the longest time line or critical path. Draw a Pareto diagram or pie chart of the total time. This of course highlights the areas of greatest opportunity for time reduction, or at least should prevent one from homing in on a relatively unimportant element.

Lead Time Map

arranged as a Gantt chart

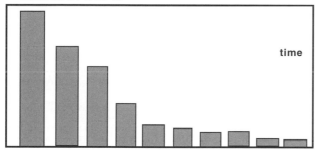

order planning

order generation

cost estimation

order receipt and entry

order selection

scheduling

manufacture

installation

billing

post sales service

time

...and as a Pareto ...

time

...and showing cross-functional responsibilities.

	sales	engineering	scheduling	manufacture	etc
order planning	C		R		
order generation	R	I		I	
cost estimation		R		I	C
order entry	R		C		I
etc.					

R = responsible   I = inform   C = consult

A further refinement is to estimate, within each category, the percentage of value adding time. Value adding time will normally be a very small percentage, so this may not be worthwhile doing.

A possible further extension is to benchmark each element. The established procedure of "best demonstrated practice" aims at finding the best performer on each element, and then combining the series of best practices into an overall best practice which is superior to any individual organisation.

ORDER MAPPING

This section deals with the mapping and improvement of customer orders. The aim is to decrease leadtime and improve customer service. Mapping and improvement of actual manufacture is only part of the whole, and in an increasing number of companies the less significant proportion of leadtime and competitiveness.

There are two approaches here: "stapling yourself to an order", and the tagging system. Very often a combination of both is best.

"STAPLING YOURSELF TO AN ORDER".

"Stapling" is very similar to overall lead time mapping, but concentrates more on the clerical processes. This simply means following through an order from receipt to dispatch. In many companies orders experience considerable delays so it is not feasible literally to "attach" yourself to an order. Shapiro et al stress the importance of tracing the full "order management cycle" from planning to post-sales service. They state that there are typically 10 steps, some of which may overlap:

→ order planning

→ order generation

→ cost estimation and pricing

→ order receipt and entry

→ order selection and prioritisation

→ scheduling

→ fulfilment (including procurement, manufacture, assembly, testing, shipping, installation)

→ billing

→ returns and claims

→ postsales service

You should walk the path of a selection of order types. This is the paper equivalent of the process activity map: simply document the steps, noting the process time, distances, and delays.

Make a sketch of the flow rather than using a formal process activity chart. Such charts are much harder for non-experts to read. Under each stage note the data collected, and add comments and queries by means of "post-it" stickers. However, when preparing the sketch, first draw broad lines (or columns if you prefer to work top to bottom) representing the various departments or physical areas through which the order passes. This is known in Business Process Reengineering language as the "as is" chart. Shapiro et al suggest drawing up a matrix chart with the 10 steps forming the rows and the various departments or functions forming the columns. Then identify who has prime responsibility for each step and who has a supporting role. Very useful.

When drawing the sketch, use different colours or shading for physical movement of paper and for flows by computer network, telephone and fax.

TAGGING

Tagging is a useful supplement to "Stapling yourself to an order". Tagging does not involve an analyst in walking the route, but relies upon employees to record data as they deal with an order or design. The idea is to collect a representative sample of data that helps track variation both in time and in routing. Do not rely only upon tagging; you need to "go to Gemba" to uncover the reality; but when combined with physical tracking a rich picture can be built up. You will need the co-operation of everyone that deals with the document in question, so plan a meeting that explains the purpose of the exercise. Do not have any hidden agendas - if you are found out, the exercise will end, with disastrous consequences for the project in general and the analyst in particular.

Tagging simply involves adding a coloured page to the document on which everyone receiving the document enters location, entry time, exit time, a brief description of the actions taken at each stage, and next stage that the order is sent on to. Tagging is a sampling procedure and a version of the well-known work study technique of activity sampling. The necessity here is to collect representative data. It is unnecessary to go into the statistics of sample sizes for confidence intervals. If you really wish to obtain data that has a known statistical level of confidence, there are formulas available in standard texts on work study. You will probably find that a sample of 20 to 30 orders is adequate. However, rather spend time on collecting and analysing good data, than merely going for volume. Common sense, as ever, is the best weapon. For instance, collect data evenly through the month not only at month end, avoid collecting data only at rush periods or on rush days, and take samples at irregular intervals. The sampling sheets need to be fed into the normal point of receipt of orders. Be aware that there may be several starting points. Having decided upon the sample size, make sure that the number started come out the far end, and don't get lost or are significantly delayed - in fact it is those that are of most interest!

A typical Tagging Sheet

Entry	Time	Location	Actions taken	Exit Time	
19/5	10.25	Sales	Book order	19/5	11:00
20/5	15:15	Scheduling	Enter on MPS	20/5	17:00
23/5	9:10	Sales	Confirm order	24/5	10:43

Etc.

Tagging collects a different sort of information from walking an order. There will be less opportunity to build a picture of the physical and human side but there will be more opportunity to analyse variation - minimum, average and maximum times and the reasons behind the variation.

Interpretation of the "Stapling" and "Tagging" information can be done using the Time Charting and Analysis principles, as given in the next section. The following should result:

➔ An assessment of the savings in lead time, often for different categories of order. Pareto analysis applies. Typically there will be enormous savings for a majority of routine orders but little saving for a small proportion. It may be worth sacrificing efficiencies on some orders for the benefit of most.

➔ An assessment of costs and benefits, but in particular the cost of reprocessing and the benefits of improved competitiveness.

➔ An assessment of the additional skills required.

➔ An assessment of the organisational implications. (Organisational politics are often an important factor)

FURTHER READING:
Benson Shapiro, Kasturi Rangan, John Sviokla, "Staple Yourself to an Order", *Harvard Business Review,* July-August 1992, pp113-122

CUSTOMER MAPPING

Customer mapping is the process of identifying your customers, and their influence, right along the demand chain. It attempts to break through the idea that customers are to be found only in the next tier of supply. It gives insight into who provides the revenue and who makes the decision to use the product. This map is a variation on the Physical Structure Map (see separate section) giving less detail on immediate suppliers and customers but more detail as to ultimate customers and their influence.

An example of a Customer Map is shown in the figure. This is for a Steel Supply Chain. Notice that the market share at each stage pertains to the original product, in this case steel, rather than to the immediate supplier. Thus each steel service centre may supply steel from several steelmakers, but the market share given for the manufacturer relates to the steelmaker not to the steel service centre.

A Customer Map will often be an approximation, due to confidentiality of information. It doesn't matter; the important point is getting the big picture.

A very useful addition is to determine, for each customer, who is the buyer, the decider, the user, the specifier. Each will have different requirements, typically variations on cost, quality, and delivery. Find them out, if possible. Then proceed Pareto-wise, to construct another four diagrams which weights these requirements by market share. See the figure.

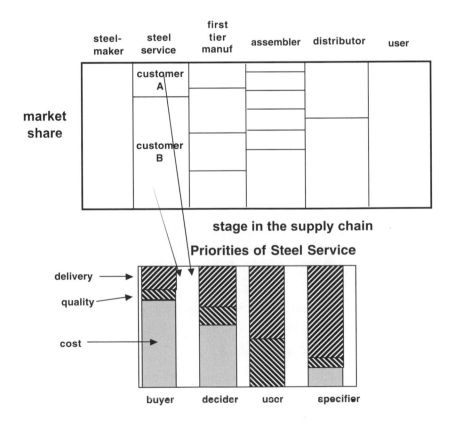

Customer Mapping

FURTHER READING:
M. McDonald and I. Dunbar, *Market Segmentation,* Macmillan, 1995

"LEARNING TO SEE" MAPPING OR PROCESS CARTOON

The "Learning to See" map or Cartoon has emerged as a very popular and clear way to illustrate the current and future state of a process. The method maps both material and information flows. It is quick to learn because it uses simple boxes to indicate stages, and other obvious symbols such as trucks, factories, and kanban cards. The tool really works best for repetitive operations, especially where a single product or family is made.

Begin with the Current State. Pick a main product. Draw a factory symbol for main Suppliers at the top left and Distribution or Customer at top right. In the top centre draw to box for Production Control. Along the bottom of the page list the main stages of manufacture, one to a box. Below each stage, in other boxes, find out and list cycle time for the chosen product, changeover time, the OEE or the percentage availability, and the available time per week. Between the stages, show the current inventory holdings in a triangle. Then draw in the material flows. Use a broad arrow for this. For supply and deliveries, draw in a truck symbol and label each with the frequency of delivery.

At the bottom of the page, draw a zig-zag line, corresponding with the production stages, to indicate the value adding time and non value adding time.

Now find out and draw in the scheduling information. Draw narrow arrows connecting the customer with Production Control to indicate forecasts and orders. Label the frequency. You can use lightning symbols to indicate electronic links. Do the same for the Supplier. Now find out how the schedule is communicated to the factory floor. Connect Production Control to the appropriate stages by narrow arrows. An example is shown.

"Learning to See" Maps

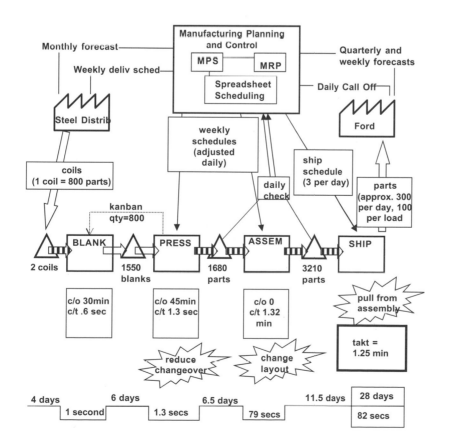

Now comes analysis. The idea is to develop a concept diagram of the future state. Many sections of this book will help. Begin with takt time. Think about appropriate batch sizes, move quantities, target changeover times, and whether pull can replace push. Look out for imbalance lines, and overproduction. Also look at future information flows to see if they can be simplified.

The point about these diagrams is that they are very clear and can be used for planning and participation meetings, from shop floor to top management. As a reference tool they can be placed on boards in meeting areas, and ideas can be added by Post-it stickers. Progress can be chartered. A powerful tool.

FURTHER READING:

Mike Rother and John Shook, *Learning to See,* The Lean Enterprise Institute, Brookline, MA, 1998 (no ISBN, but fax on USA 617 713 2999).

PROCESS ACTIVITY MAPPING

The process activity map is the well known process flow chart. This is also the first of the "Seven Tools of Quality". The origins are, of course, in work study and industrial engineering. Recently, however, with the advent of business process reengineering and JIT these process charts have gained renewed interest, but with the difference that who now uses them are not just the work study officers or I.E.s but supervisors and operators as well. In fact, the first preference is for operators to learn how to use this most effective tool themselves. For an external change agent, following the process in detail gives credibility and confidence and helps prevent naive solutions. Importantly, process activity mapping helps identify opportunities.

A particular concern that has emerged over the last decade is to do with value-adding and non value adding activities. The process chart is the prime tool for such analysis.

The process chart lists every step that is involved in the manufacture of a product or the delivery of a service. Standard symbols are used to indicate "operation", "delay", "move", "store", and "inspect". (See figure). The process chart helps identify wasteful actions, and documents the process completely. Good communication is an important reason to do this. The systematic record helps reveal the possible sources of quality and productivity problems.

Many companies already have process charts. If they are available, beware! There are often differences between the "official" process charts and the way things actually happen in practice. Are they up to date? The team or analyst should take the time to follow through a number of products, services or customers, documenting any "horror stories" that occur. Often several actions and "rework loops", unknown to management will be discovered. But it is not the purpose of the chart to use it for "policing". Often a team will draw up a chart for their own use in improvement and should not be obliged to turn it over to management.

CONSTRUCTING THE PROCESS MAP

Some process maps or charts can be long and complicated. If so, first break them up into sections of responsibility or physical areas. So start from a Block Diagram or Learning to See chart.

Then begin the detailed recording. See the figure. Preferably use a verb and a noun (e.g. select part, or verify document), and decide which of the standard categories (operation, transport / move, inspect, delay, store) the activity fits into. (Note : the difference between delay and store, is that store takes place in a specific store area or warehouse, whereas delay is a result of an in-process stoppage such as waiting for a stillage to fill up). You may also differentiate between value adding and non-value adding operations.

Step	Description	Symbol	Time	Inventory	People	Machine	Notes
1	unload truck	O	8 min	4000 pieces	2	forklift	
2	place at bay	D	3 min	2000 ave	0		temp store
3	move to line	⇒	1.6 min / trip	1000 per trip	1	forklift	4 trips
4	store at line	▽	330	4000	0		
5	press	O	0.06 / piece	1	1	A220 press	batch of 4000
6	store in container	D	12 min	2000			

Whilst compiling the process chart it is good to record distance, time, inventory, and the number of operators. (If you are skilled at work study, also "rate" the speed of work, but this is a secondary benefit.) Also, record any wastes, comments, or interesting events. Some process chart compilers also use a Polaroid or digital camera. Whilst going around, take note of dates on inventory control cards, levels of dust, and container discipline (are containers moved in a first in first out , or a last in first out sequence?). You may encounter some carousels where parts are moved or stored automatically. If so, mark them (unobtrusively if necessary) to get an idea of the length of storage or delay.

A process map is a "snapshot" of activity at a moment in time. Of course, workloads and inventory levels may vary over the course of a month, and hence delay times may change. Record the actual figure that you observe, but you may also ask about minimum and maximum levels. Most parts are made in batches, so you should try to record the average length of time to make one of the parts. For instance, where a container is being filled at the end of a process, record the length of delay that the median (middle) part will spend in the container before being moved.

A most useful exercise is to track one particular part, not just the type of part. However, this is often not practical due to the length of delays. So, mark a few parts and then come back and track their progress. Most manufactured parts have several branches or subassemblies flowing into the main sequence. It is a good idea to check on this first. Begin with the "main sequence". Then give attention to the major feeders, by time or cost, although it will seldom be necessary to track all feeders.

Also, you can "black box" a particular sequence of operations. (There is a special symbol to indicate this.) Very often, after you have analysed the charts, you may decide to come back and do a far more detailed micro analysis of these process steps. Take particular care of inspection and rework points. Why is this necessary? Can it be done earlier? What happens to reject parts ? In work study there are more detailed charting or mapping techniques available, such as the two handed flow process chart, but don't go into these unless you have identified the particular step as an important bottleneck.

For supply chain purposes, it is especially useful to record the same product as it flows through several plants or stages. If possible, let the same person or team track throughout its journey along the supply chain.

In service businesses, but also in some customer interface manufacturing locations, process charts can be made more effective by differentiating between front office and back office operations. You may consider using Service Blueprinting. A more detailed description is given in the section of Service Blueprinting in our book *The Quality 60.*

ANALYSING THE PROCESS MAP

The process activity map forms the basis of several types of analysis. For instance, by adding cost data it is the basis of Cost Time profile mapping. (See separate section.) But analysing the basic chart or map allows one to

➜   obtain the proportion of value adding time

➜   obtain the time split between the various activities (see the figure).

➜   highlight any immediate problems or surprises

➜   identify, via a Pareto analysis, the areas of greatest opportunity

➜   record or benchmark the current status

Once this general analysis has been completed, you should probe into further opportunities. There are four possibilities for each step :

➜ it adds (external) customer value. These should be retained. Note that not every "operation" step adds value, although transport, delay, store, inspect, rework definitely do not add customer value).

➜ it adds process value (for instance changeover time, SPC, planning, evaluation, etc) which are currently necessary for the process, but do not add to customer value. Such activities are waste, but temporarily necessary waste. Aim to reduce then eliminate.

➜ it adds business value (for instance, it benefits managers, employees, and suppliers). These too are waste, and need to be critically examined for efficiency or elimination.

➜ It adds service value (for instance, repackaging in a mail order business.) Such activities may be waste in some companies, but not in others. Simplify and reduce.

➜ it adds no value. These should be eliminated as soon as possible, or continuously reduced (as with transport).

If you are concerned with implementing JIT or one-piece-flow (and who shouldn't be?) it is good to have an idea of the "takt" time. Operators working faster than takt are either overproducing (muda!) or should be spending part of their day doing other things. Find out which is the case. If they are working much slower than the takt time, how is the system coping (overtime? assisted working?). Some analysts distinguish between cycle time (the time between units), and the work time (the time actually working). The difference is waste, or rest, or imbalance, or waiting for machine. There may be opportunity for combining or rationalising work.

In general, the steps should then be analysed using the 5 Whys (asking why 5 times over to get to the root cause - see separate section) and with the aid of Rudyard Kipling's "Six Honest Serving Men" (who taught me all I knew; their names are what and why and when, and who and where and how).

Thereafter, the creative or redesign phase begins. Some "mechanical" considerations are :

➜ can inspection steps be moved forward or eliminated ?

➜ can steps be done in parallel ?

➜ are there obvious candidates for automation ?

➜ is data being duplicated ? is it effectively shared ?

➜ can pre-preparation be done, before the event ?

➜ can steps be moved to another stage? (for instance, can a supplier take over a non-core stage?)

Michael Hammer has some useful non-mechanical suggestions concerning assumptions. The following is based on his "Out-of-the box thinking".

Are you assuming a specialist must do the work ? (People).
Are you assuming that purchasing will pay only after receiving an invoice ? (Time).
Are you assuming that record keeping must be done in the office ? (Place).
Are you assuming that inventory is required for better service ? (Resources).
Are you assuming that the customer should not be involved ? (Customer).

(See also the sections "Time Charting and Analysis" and "Business Process Mapping")

SELECTED FURTHER READING:

Diane Galloway, *Mapping Work Processes,* ASQC Quality Press, Milwaukee, 1994, ISBN 0-87389-266-6

William Trischler, *Understanding and Applying Value Added Assessment,* ASQC Quality Press, 1996, ISBN 0-87389-369-7

AT&T Quality Steering Committee, *Reengineering Handbook,* Indianapolis,1991 (for Hammer's "Out-of-the box Thinking" see p 106) ISBN 0-932764-36-3

George Stalk Jr. and Thomas Hout, *Competing Against Time,* Free Press, New York, 1990, Chapters 6 and 7. ISBN 0-02-915291-7

PRODUCT VARIETY FUNNEL

The product variety funnel is useful in understanding where variety is added along a supply chain. The principle is that variety should be added as late as possible; adding variety too early cuts responsiveness, adds inventory, and reduces flexibility. This has much in common with ideas on Mass Customisation and Product Platforms (see separate sections). It could also be seen as the map for "Set-Based" Concurrent Engineering (see separate section).

For instance, consider the manufacture of an axle assembly that has 60 steps. A manufacturer may decide to make a unique axle for each engine type and for each market. The customer expectation of lead time means that axles will have to be started for particular engines and markets on a forecast basis, which will often be wrong. This adds waste. But, say the axles can be redesigned such that the first 40 steps are common for all engines and markets. Now the forecast need only be made for the total build, which is far more likely to be correct. Waste is cut, and response time improves.

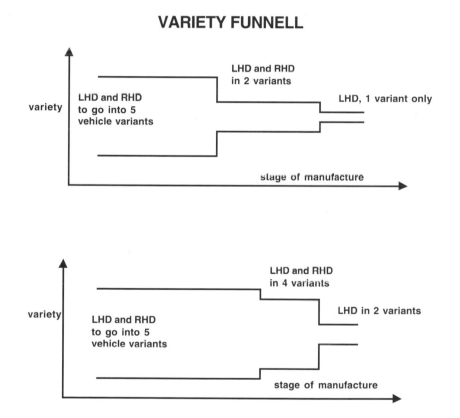

So the map traces the production steps or stage against the retained variety. See the figure. The map is very useful for future product planning and design strategy purposes. A goal may be set to extend the variety forward by x stages in y time. This may mean changes in design, or in manufacturing technology, or in process / layout design.

This map can be used within one company or may extend to the full supply chain. Of course, it requires co-operation to attack the problems, but the map is a useful first step.

Consider an automotive supply chain example. A metal bracket is made in left and right hand drive versions. Although a common steel is used, variety may be retained in blanking (done at a steel service centre), or onto first stage pressing (done at a fabricator), or onto various stages in welding and assembly (done at the first tier supplier). Since overall demand for left and right hand versions is more stable than for the versions separately, especially over the short term, there are big implications for flow and inventories in the supply chain. Refer to the figure on the previous page.

QUALITY FILTER MAPPING

Quality filter mapping is a form of run diagram, one of the least used but highest potential "7 tools" of quality. Quality filter mapping aims to pick up the rate and sources of defect along a supply chain. Of course, not all defects are passed onto the final customer, due to internal rejection and rework, but all are waste. Hines and Rich identify three types of defect :

➔ Product defects that are not caught by the producer, but are passed onto the next customer, whether internal or external. Usually this would be monitored between supply chain partners.

➔ Service defects are not found in the products themselves, but result from errors in paperwork, late or wrong deliveries, wrong specifications, orders, data entry or communications, and the like.

➔ Internal scrap and rework result from errors that are picked up by the producer but are not passed onto the next customer.

These three types of defect are mapped onto a diagram showing defects along the vertical axis and the supply chain stages horizontally. Note that defects should be recorded not only at points where the company records defects, but also at all operation steps. This is to ensure picking up what Juran refers to as "chronic" wastes (the underlying defects, reworks, or inspections that have become so routine that they are not recognised as a problem). An example is the 100% manual touch-up welds done at the end of a robotic assembly line, which enjoyed zero priority for improvement but which, upon analysis proved to be one of the most costly quality problems in the plant.

In particular, such mapping can highlight defects that are passed over long distances along a supply chain only to be rejected beyond the point at which return for rework is not economic. Also, defective parts that are passed onto bottleneck machines, thereby wasting capacity.

Beware also of believing a company's official defective figures. 5 ppm may be the result of excellent process control, or of numerous inspections and reworks. In 1995 the story was told of a famous German car whose average time for rectification exceeded the total time required to build an entire new Toyota Carina. The final build quality of the German car was, however, superb.

DEMAND AMPLIFICATION MAPPING

This tool maps what is termed the "Forrester Effect" after Jay Forrester of MIT who first modelled the amplification of disturbances along the supply chain and illustrated the effect in supply chain games. It is also a form of the well-known run diagram used in quality management, but here shows production activities against time. Refer also to the section on System Dynamics.

Amplification is the enemy of linear production and lean manufacturing, and results from batching and inventory control policies applied along the supply chain. For instance, fairly regular or linear customer demand is translated into batch orders by a retailer, then subject to further modification by a distributor adjusting safety stocks, then amplified further by a manufacturer who may have long changeovers and big batches, and then further modified by a supplier who orders in yet larger batches to get quantity discounts. The result is that, further along the chain, the pattern of demand in no way resembles the final customer demand.

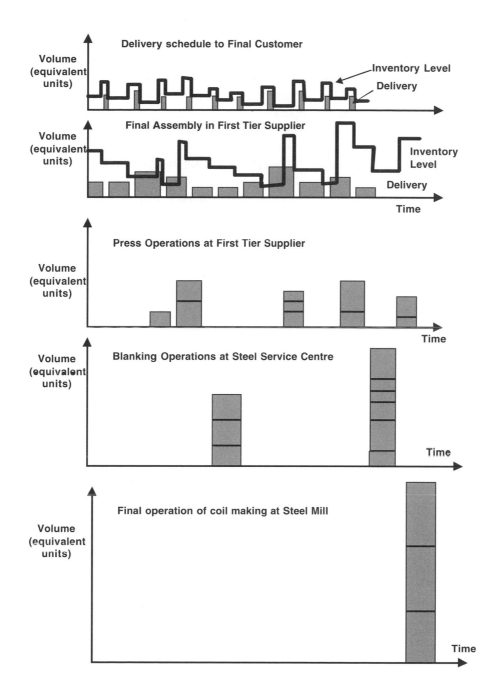

This mapping tool can be used in two ways: for a single member of a supply chain and for a complete supply chain. In the former case the graph shows actual customer orders, manufacturing orders, and orders placed on the next stage of manufacture, plotted against time. In the latter case it shows the demands placed by each tier in the supply chain on the next tier, shown against time. Examples are shown on the next page. It is also useful to show inventory levels against time on the same graphs.

A useful addition, for analysis purposes, is to have each demand line shown on a separate transparent film that can be slid along to allow for lead-time delays. A further useful addition is to include inventory levels in the diagram. It may be discovered that the rise and fall of inventory levels are out of sync with the order policies, resulting in too much inventory, or unnecessary orders at particular times. Although many companies have this data, it is unusual for them to show the information on a graph. The map is excellent at revealing any dislocations that occur within a company or along a whole supply chain.

Of course, this tool is provocative in asking what can be done : faster (EDI ? EPOS?) communication, not over-reacting or deliberate under-reaction, better long term demand visibility, synchronised manufacture, passing final demands several stages down the supply chain, DRP, policies on stability, cross-docking, or milk-round deliveries are some of the possibilities. See the section on Quick Response. See the figure.

REFERENCE:

PICSIE Books, The Buckingham Supply Chain Game, PICSIE Books, Buckingham, 1997 (revised 1999).
Padmanabhan Lee and Wang, "The Paralyzing Curse of the Bullwhip Effect in a Supply Chain", *Sloan Management Review,* April 1997, pp93-102

PUSH PULL MAPPING

Push Pull Mapping (called Decision Point Analysis by Hines and Rich) maps the point at which push meets pull. From a lean enterprise perspective, it is desirable to pull products through a supply chain, dependent upon customer demand - in other words to create demand pull rather than supply push. Pull reduces inventories and overproduction, and encourages flow - see the section on Lean Thinking. However, pull throughout the full supply chain is often not practised, and may not be possible in the short or medium term. Push Pull mapping identifies the points or buffers, within companies and taking the chain as a whole, where push takes over from pull. This is useful because

➜   the pull point should be moved further back along the supply chain; one should set up a strategy to move towards this over time.

➜   a challenge is set asking why push exists and how can it be changed

➜   if supply chains are to work they must become demand flow chains, even if this means that there are intermediate buffers which signal the previous stage to stop or start work.

➜   the vision is synchronisation; what a supplier makes today is used tomorrow by a customer, all along the chain.

PUSH - PULL ANALYSIS

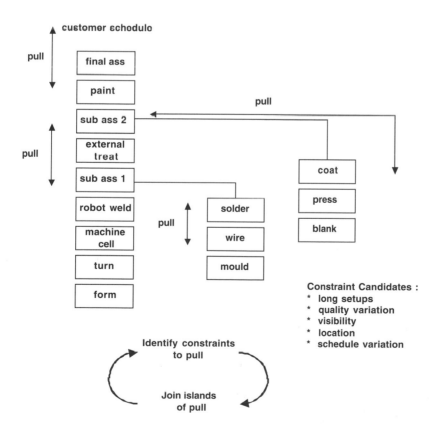

For instance, in an automotive press shop making small metal parts, final packaging is often pulled from the car manufacturer via frequent kanbans. The next stage back, final assembly, may or may not be subject to pull. If not, why not ? the reasons may be lack of cells, poor communication, scheduling difficulties or whatever. But, there are not long setups involved so converting to pull should be relatively easy. Before assembly is pressing. Here longer changeovers or tooling difficulties may be the reason why pull is not being done. Even with long changeovers, pull may be possible to fill gaps in buffers. Before pressing comes blanking. Can this stage be linked via pull to pressing? Perhaps, even though assembly and pressing cannot be linked by pull, can blanking and pressing be synchronised ?

PHYSICAL STRUCTURE MAPPING

Physical structure mapping helps set the policy for supplier and customer rationalisation. At each stage in the supply chain, you simply list how many suppliers and how many customers there are, by type and by value added or spend. See the figure.

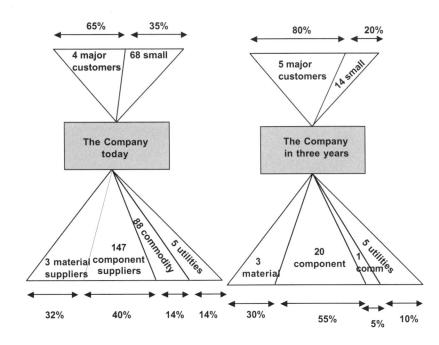

This is useful for

→ benchmarking - for instance, lean plants tend to have fewer suppliers but a smaller proportion of total value added

→ looking at all suppliers - even though a company may have reduced its supply base for components, have similar rationalisations taken place with utilities and office commodities?

→ looking at all customers - has the company done a Pareto on its customer base, is there a long tail of marginally profitable or unprofitable customers ?

Notice that the figure shows the present situation and future planned situation. Drawing the map brings these planning issues to light.

CAPACITY MAPPING

The mapping tools discussed so far have all been maps of product flow from raw material to final customer. But what about resources that are used for several products ? Capacity demand mapping looks at ratio of capacity demanded to total capacity available. The idea is to identify the physical bottlenecks and constraints along the supply chain. The ideas of Goldratt are most relevant here, particularly the Drum, Buffer, Rope and the Five steps of the Theory of Constraints. These are discussed in separate sections.

A true constraint literally prevents the company or supply chain making more money, and these constraints may not be to do with the physical capacity at all. However, there will inevitably be differences in available physical capacity along the supply chain. The idea here is to identify where these constraints lie. Be aware of two types : each company along a supply chain will have a most highly constrained resource, and the supply chain as a whole will have a most constrained resource.

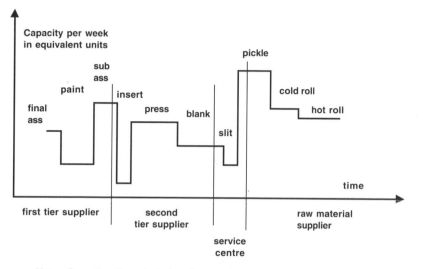

Note : Operation times include subsequent storage and transport

Capacity demand mapping should distinguish between operations time, changeover time, and maintenance time. (See also the section on TPM dealing with the 6 big losses). Time is the common unit that should be used, not product units. It also should account, at constrained workcentres, for normal and maximum work throughput rates. Then load should be shown on the map. The current available time should be calculated by allowing for current maintenance practice and the current number of changeovers. See the figure. (Capacity is what is available for use under normal conditions, load is the hours of work that is scheduled to be done at the workcentre during a comparable period.)

Capacity mapping will give an immediate impression of the difficulties of establishing flow. A rule of thumb is that where load exceeds about 80% of maximum current available capacity, flow operations will be difficult and queues may be the norm. This does not mean that the situation is incapable of resolution - it does mean that the urgency for constraint management, and for synchronised bottleneck planning is urgent.

Demand flow is only possible by planning around the constraints. The first priority should be to synchronise operations at the company level, then to synchronise the chain. Synchronising the chain is a big challenge, requiring partnership co-operation. By mapping we know what information links are vital for the whole supply chain to work well; the minimum is a link from final customer demand to the most constrained workcentre, and a link from this workcentre to the "gateway" workcentre of the entire chain.

A family of charts can be drawn

→ Stacked bar charts showing total changeover time, total run time, total downtime, and total idle time for each stage

→ A bar chart showing total idle time for each stage

→ A graph, or family of graphs, showing
  → idle time / (changeover + run time)
  → downtime / (changeover + run time)
  → idle time / changeover time

After you have identified those resources that are most constrained, it is a good idea to go back and look at these resources in more detail. A second round of data collection is desirable, but focused only on the critical resources. This second tranche of data will act both as a verification of the previous data as well as giving an indication of variation. Always "Go to Gemba", that is, visit the resource in person and spend at least an hour watching and noting.

INTERPRETING CAPACITY MAPS

➔ The first thing to identify is the relative constraints or bottlenecks. A good indication is given by the idle time bar chart. Beware, however, of variation. A production stage having a moderate amount of idle time, but having significant variance is usually more troublesome than a process having low idle time but also low variance. Look at constraints and bottlenecks in relation to the graph of idle time as a proportion of setup plus run time; where this ratio is low, particular care should be taken.

➔ Capacity maps become particularly useful when looked at with Demand Amplification maps. Here you would like to examine if it is possible to run more frequent, smaller batches. Stages at which there is the greatest potential for doing this are indicated by the graph showing the idle time / changeover time ratio. The higher the ratio, the greater the potential.

➔ A more involved, but very useful calculation, is to try to determine the most constrained resources in the full supply chain. The ratio you are looking for is idle time per product. Here it is necessary to use conversion factors. For instance if a coil of steel makes 800 products then the idle time in coil stages should be multiplied by 800. The most constrained resource or resources, of course, should become the priority targets for improvement activities and are also the resources that need most careful scheduling and monitoring. In line with the OPT philosophy, such resources need to kept as busy as possible ("an hour lost at a bottleneck is an hour lost for the whole system" according to Goldratt), and protected by "time buffer" stock.

COST TIME PROFILE

A Cost Time Profile is simply a graph showing accumulated cost against accumulated time. Its beauty lies in its visual impact which, the writer can verify, often leaves senior managers stunned. Whenever value or cost is added, the graph moves upwards; a plateau indicates no value or cost being added for a period of time, for instance during delay or storage. The area under the graph represents the time that money is tied up for. The aim is to reduce the area under the graph by reducing time and/or cost. The technique is superior to a simple Pareto analysis of cost and time accumulations because one can immediately recognise where expensive inventory is lying idle and at what stage time delays occur. An example is shown in the figure.

Notice two cumulative lines, one for total cost and the other for value. The difference between these two lines represents wasteful, non value adding activities and other cost accumulations such as the cost of money being tied up in inventory. Non value adding activities include inspections, transport, clerical activities, and rework. A cost time profile can be obtained directly from the process activity map, by multiplying by the costs of the various resources. If the process activity map is recorded on a spreadsheet, the calculations for the cost time profiles are easily done. When this is done, however, note that waste may still exist in a nominally value adding operation - for instance wasteful movements in an assembly activity, so that the lower profile does not represent the ultimate aim. The vertical distance between the two lines represents some obvious wastes, but not all wastes. For example, the long plateaux also represent waste of unnecessary storage and inventory. The aim should be to gradually reduce the profile towards that shown in the bottom left hand corner of the figure.

Cost Time Profile

Note that when bought in materials are added, this results in a vertical bar on the chart equal to the material cost. In practice, the time for most value adding operations is minuscule in comparison with the delay and queue times, so value adding operations also appear as a vertical jump.

So a Cost Time Profile is a graphical method to identify when and where costs accumulate. They have been used extensively in conjunction with lean manufacturing, supply chain analysis, business process reengineering and total quality. Look for long plateaux, especially later on in the process where costs have already accumulated. Attacking the long time plateaux will reduce cost, and improve responsiveness and quality.

The profiles are relevant to quality improvement because there is often a direct correlation between poor quality and wasted time. So for instance when there are delays due to rework, inspection or queuing, both costs and time accumulates. Many customers associate good quality with shorter response or delivery times. The technique has been extensively used and developed by Westinghouse who used it as part of their Baldridge award-winning performance. It is equally applicable in manufacturing or office environments.

Westinghouse made extensive use of cost time profile charts, but presumably this is not what caused the break-up of the company in 1997! The company used the profiles in a hierarchical fashion. That is the profile for each sub-process or product can be combined to form a profile for a whole section which in turn can be combined into a profile for a complete plant or division. Here total costs are used, so it is necessary to multiply the unit cost profiles by the average number of units in process. All processes must be considered; value adding as well as support activities and overheads. This therefore represents a total process view of the organisation, and may therefore be used with process reengineering or Hoshin planning.

FURTHER READING:
Jack H Fooks, *Profiles for Performance: Total Quality Methods for Reducing Cycle Time,* Addison Wesley, Reading, MA, 1993, ISBN 0-201-56314-2

BUSINESS PROCESS MAPPING

Business Process Mapping has gained much attention in the 1990s with BPR. We should however note that this activity is not new: Joseph Juran mapped work processes for the U.S. government's war support activities in 1941, reducing the time to clear a requisition from 90 days to 53 hours. (Butman, 1997). This section should also be read with the sections on Business Process Reengineering and Time Charting and Analysis.

There are many variations of business process mapping, but most concentrate on the office or service sector, and deal with workflow. Business process mapping has much in common with Learning to See Mapping and Process Activity Mapping, with a few differences :

➜ an important feature is that the flows between departments or areas of responsibility are shown. Usually, departments are shown in columns with time and actions shown from top to bottom of page. The flows between departments are thus clearly seen. This is at the heart of BPR, which sees organisation by cross-departmental process, rather than within departments or "silos".

➜ often, the standard work study symbols are not used. Instead, simple squares and rectangles are used. Decision points are often shown as triangles. However, icons or graphic symbols may be used to illustrate people, computers, desks, filing cabinets, etc.

➜ often, the different types of flows (material, information, and paper) are shown on the same diagram using different line symbols, as in Learning to See.

➜ it is quite possible to have two levels of detail. An overview diagram may simply show the flow of documents between departments without any detail, whilst a fully detailed diagram may home in on specific parts or be used by different analysts.

In BPR it is common to show both "as is" and "should be" diagrams.

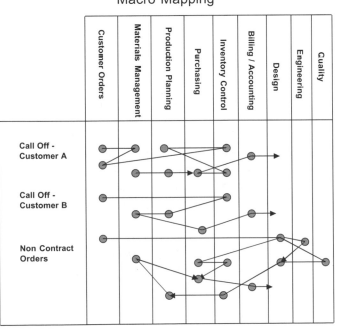

Business Process Reengineering :
Macro Mapping

Variations :
* plot time on the vertical axis
* add Post-It notes to nodes
* label the flows with document types
* add supporting photographs

An example is shown in the figure overleaf. Here, only the macro map is drawn, without the detail found in more extensive maps. However, this may be sufficient particularly if complete redesign is contemplated. All of the comments on analysis made in the process activity mapping section are applicable in business process mapping.

One important variation is " IDEFO" or "structured analysis and design technique" (also known as "triple diagonal modelling"). These are important because they have been adopted as the standard requirement for various government departments (for example the U.S. Department of Defence), and by some major companies. The good news is that such mapping is very thorough and well established, the bad news is that it is cumbersome and takes time to learn. A full explanation of IDEFO is not feasible for this book. Please consult the references.

FURTHER READING:

Gary Born, *Process Management to Quality Improvement,* Wiley, Chichester, 1994, ISBN 0-471-94283-9
Raymond Manganelli and Mark Klein, *The REengineering Handbook,* AmaCom, New York, 1994, ISBN 0-8144-7923-5

Institute Of Business Process Reengineering
1 Cecil Court, London Road, Enfield, Middlesex, EN2 3AF Tel 0181 366 6718

TIME CHARTING AND ANALYSIS

Time charting is a recent procedure that has arisen with the realisation of the importance of time as a "competitive weapon". Time based competition recognises that many customers value time, consider it an important dimension of quality, and are often prepared to pay a premium for a product or service delivered in less time.

It turns out that often there is a direct relationship between time taken and quality levels, but in the opposite way to what many people think. Reducing the time to make a product leads to less work in process and quicker detection of any problems that may have arisen. So defective processes can be stopped sooner and the amount of rework is reduced. The same effect is found in services; reducing the time often improves the feedback and leads to improvement before what has taken place is forgotten.

Time charting and analysis can be used in reducing manufacturing lead times, reducing product development times, and improving the turnaround in virtually any service industry. The procedure has much in common with the use of the "7 tools", but is worth specific mention because the aims go well beyond the removal of quality problems.

The critical path technique (CPA) has been used for over 40 years for project management, essentially to arrange the time co-ordination of a variety of activities. Versions of CPA do allow for "crashing"; that is the deliberate reduction of project time by using additional resources. This is a trade-off; less time for more cost. But in time charting and analysis the aim is to reduce time without an additional cost penalty or in fact to reduce both time and cost.

Time charting and analysis begins by assembling a process activity chart (see the separate section) or a critical path diagram which details all the steps involved in producing the product or service. The process chart must contain the elapsed time data. The standard process chart uses standardised symbols to indicate operation, move, delay/wait, and store. These should be used because they aid clarity. (There are also variations of the process chart, such as the man-machine chart that can be useful. Details are given in specialised books on work-study, but are usually not necessary for the purpose described here.)

Often in manufacturing, but also in services, there is an "official" process chart (what should happen) and a real process chart (what actually happens). Also process charts, where they are kept, are often notoriously out of date. In any case the aim is to get the real time-process chart. This can often be achieved by following through a product or service and detailing all the steps and times, including delays and storage.

Now the questioning begins. The aim is to reduce time and waste. It is essentially a creative process. Preferably the people involved in the process should be used in its analysis and improvement. Bold thinking is a requirement, not piecemeal adjustment. The title of the classic article in Harvard Business Review by Michael Hammer gives the clue: "Reengineering work: don't automate, obliterate!"; that is the type of thinking that is required. Competitive benchmarking may be useful as may the creativity encouraged by value engineering. The same Harvard Business Review article tells of how Ford used to have 400 accounts payable clerks compared with just 7 people at Mazda.

The basic step is to examine the process chart and to split the activities into those that add immediate value for the customer and those that do not. Refer to the "7 wastes" for guidance. The concept is to achieve the added value of the product or service in as small a time as possible. Therefore try to make every value-adding step continuous with the last value-adding step, without interruptions for waiting, queuing, or for procedures which assist the company but not the customer. Stalk refers to this as the "main sequence". There are several guidelines:

→ Can the non-value adding steps be eliminated, simplified, or reduced?

→ Can any activities that delay a value adding activity be simplified or rescheduled?

→ Are there any activities, particularly non value adding activities, which can be done in parallel with the sequence of value adding activities?

→ Can activities that have to be passed from department to department (and back!) be reorganised into a team activity? Better still, can one person do it? (What training and backup would be required?)

→ Where are the bottlenecks? Can the capacity of the bottleneck be expanded? Do bottleneck operations keep working, or are they delayed for minor reasons? (According to Eli Goldratt, author of "The Goal" - a book on managing bottlenecks - "an hour lost at a bottleneck is an hour lost for the whole system" and "an hour lost at a non-bottleneck is merely a mirage".) Are bottleneck operations delayed by non-bottleneck operations, whether value adding or not?

→ What preparations can be made before the main sequence of value adding steps is initiated so as to avoid delays? (e.g. preparing the paperwork, getting machines ready.)

→ Can the necessary customer variety or requirements be added at a later stage? (e.g. making a basic product or service but adding the "colour and sunroof" as late as possible.)

→ If jobs are done in batches, can the batches be split so as to move on to a second activity before the whole batch is complete at the first activity?

→ Can staff flexibility be improved so as to allow several tasks to be done by one person, thus cutting handing-on delays?

→ What is the decision making arrangement? Can decision making power be devolved to the point of use? Can the routine decisions be recognised so that they can be dealt with on the spot? (Perhaps "expert systems" can be used.)

→ Where is the best place, from a time point of view, to carry out each activity? (Can the activity be carried out at the point of use or contact, or must it really be referred elsewhere?)

→ Do customers enjoy a "one stop" process? If not, why not?

→ If problems do develop, what will be the delays and how can these delays be minimised?

→ What availability of information will make the value adding sequence smoother or more continuous? (Is there more than one source of information, and if so can this be brought to one place? A common database perhaps?) The established data processing principle is to capture information only once, and let everyone use the same data.

→ As a second priority, can the time taken for value adding activities be reduced?

→ Linked with time charting and analysis should be an educational effort to make employees aware of the importance of time, and the competitive advantage that time allows. Time is a waste that can be attacked by the concerted participation effort of all employees, not just the time analysts.

→ And, of course, time measurement must become part of the process. "What gets measured gets done" is always valid. The same is true of rewards and bonus arrangements.

FURTHER READING:
Eli Goldratt and Jeff Cox, *The Goal,* Creative Output, 1986
George Stalk and Thomas Hout, *Competing Against Time,* The Free Press, New York, 1990

Soft Systems Methodology

The soft systems methodology (SSM) has been designed to tackle "soft" problems, that is to say problem areas where quantification is not appropriate and the problem area is only loosely defined. The problem is often to find the problem. A manager may know that "things are not what they should be" but finds it hard to pin down the problem due to a complex of interacting factors (in other words, a system). Of course, most real world problems are of this type.

SSM was developed by Peter Checkland and has been explained in several books. (By the way, Checkland is regarded as a real "Guru" in Japan, much less so at home in England, and almost unheard of in the USA. Sound like pre-1980 Deming?). SSM has been used in many parts of industry but also in services and government. It is a tool for improvement rather than solution, since "solutions" are seldom found in unstructured situations. It is for systems (collections of interacting parts, people, information, and so on), rather than for quantifiable problems.

SOFT SYSTEMS METHODOLOGY

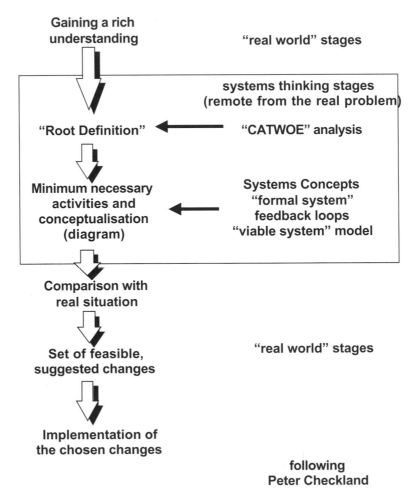

Gaining a rich understanding

"real world" stages

systems thinking stages (remote from the real problem)

"Root Definition" ← "CATWOE" analysis

Minimum necessary activities and conceptualisation (diagram)

Systems Concepts "formal system" feedback loops "viable system" model

Comparison with real situation

Set of feasible, suggested changes

"real world" stages

Implementation of the chosen changes

following Peter Checkland

Finding out

SSM begins with the rather vague activity of "finding out". The idea is to build up a rich understanding of this "thing" we are about to analyse. This may take many forms: market research, briefings by managers, inputs from customer focus groups, trends and projections from specialists and consultants, historic data, published information, and simply walking around. The Nominal Group Technique (NGT) may be useful.

INPUT OUTPUT DIAGRAMS

The first specific step is to draw one or more input-output diagrams. These diagrams show the "transformations" that the system is concerned with. For example using people, machines, money, and components to produce products. Clearly one can be much more specific, and the more specific the better. Begin by identifying the process that undertakes the transformation. Name it. Now add all the "inputs" into the process and the "outputs" from the process. It is often useful to distinguish between the actual outputs and the desirable outputs. Also, distinguish between those inputs and outputs over which there is control and those where there is none. A useful question may be to ask who are the "victims", "beneficiaries" and customers. In drawing these diagrams one is forced to think about just where the system begins and ends; this does not necessarily coincide with the organisational groupings. Input output diagramming is really an attempt to clarify the process or system with which the team is dealing. Of course it is possible to think in terms of a hierarchy of input output diagrams. There may be an overall transformation within which is located several interacting transformations. But often, at this stage it is not necessary to think through the detail. As a rule of thumb, do not have more than four sub- input-output diagrams.

THE ROOT DEFINITION

The next step is the writing down of a statement that Checkland refers to as the "root definition". This is not an aim or objective but rather a description of what the system does or hopes to do. It may begin with the words, "a system to ....". Some managers would prefer the term "mission" to "root definition". A root definition should attempt to capture the essence and richness of the situation. The root definition may run to several sentences and include mention of the customers, the people (or "actors") involved, the transformations (inputs to outputs) that it seeks to achieve, the "world view" or philosophy of the system, the "owners" of the system or the problem, and the environment in which the system operates. (Checkland uses the mnemonic CATWOE to recall these features). The reasons for the existence and continuation of the system would usually be incorporated. A root definition can be developed in several ways. Often a group process will be involved. Group discussion is usually required and techniques such as Nominal Group may be useful.

CONCEPTUALISATION

From the root definition comes the system conceptualisation. This is put together by asking, "what are the minimum necessary activities for this root definition?" (or mission). Note the words here: we are concerned with activities, so use a verb and a noun (e.g. "transfer information"). And these should be the minimum ones that are necessary. Very importantly these activities are derived directly from the root definition or mission and not from the actual situation. The Conceptualisation is an opportunity for creative synthesis, of "what might be", not a description of "what is" at the moment. The reality of the real situation must be kept apart. The only guidance is from the root definition itself.

The conceptualisation must show the interactions between the parts. Usually a diagram is drawn with the activities written inside "balloons" and the interconnections between balloons shown by means of arrows. Different types of arrow may be used to denote information, materials, customers, and other flows. A boundary may be drawn around all the balloons to indicate what is inside and what is outside the system. Then the flows (people, money, materials, customers, satisfaction, etc.) into and out of the system are drawn in. It is useful to show where these flows come from and where they go. Also identify on the diagram what the major external influences are. The measures of performance used by activities or by parts of the system may be included.

To summarise, the conceptualisation is a creative synthesis showing the activities, boundaries, interconnections, flows, and influences. An important idea is that the concept is holistic; it does not seek out specific improvements to subsystems before the full concept is complete.

COMPARISON AND RECOMMENDATION

The conceptualisation is an abstract exercise. Now comes a systematic comparison with the actual situation. The team "returns to the real world" and begins to list what changes are feasible and practical. What activities are shown in the concept and what are found in practice? Do the information flows correspond? Are the organisational groupings correct?

In the "real world" it is common that structures have evolved that result in product or information flows that double back on themselves or where responsibility for a task is split between several sections. The conceptualisation can be broken down into "subsystems" that work together more closely than with other subsystems. Because the conceptualisation has proceeded from the root definition it should overcome the problem of artificial boundaries that may exist within real organisation. For quality management this is often very important; for instance, should purchasing be part of manufacturing? ; how should design work closer with marketing? These queries should benefit from the analysis, insights, creativity, and holistic nature of the previous stages, leading to a list of suggestions for change.

The strength of this methodology, as against a pure creativity exercise, is the disciplined structure that the analysis brings. The ideas generated are not random, but are seen in context with other requirements and constraints.

FURTHER READING:
Peter Checkland, *Systems Thinking, Systems Practice,* Wiley, Chichester, 1981
Brian Wilson, *Systems : Concepts, Methodologies, and Applications,* Wiley, Chichester, 1986
Peter Checkland and Jim Scholes, *Soft Systems Methodology in Action,* Wiley, Chichester, 1990
Peter Checkland and Sue Holwell, *Information, Systems, and Information Systems,* Wiley, Chichester, 1997, ISBN 0-471-95820-4

SELF AUDITS

In this section we review three audit procedures for Lean / Just-in-Time manufacturing: by Kobayashi, Schonberger, and Fisher. Such self-evaluation questionnaires are useful both for identifying areas of opportunity or weakness and for guidance on implementation. Kobayashi's system is classic Japanese, concentrating on shop floor management. Schonberger's goes wider bringing in customers, benchmarking and perhaps a more Western view of employees. Fisher's is perhaps the classic APICS view, integrating JIT with other manufacturing systems, particularly MRPII.

Lascelles and Peacock point out that there are several approaches to self-assessment. Award Simulation involves writing a full submission as if applying for an award. Peer involvement uses an in-house team to write their own assessment using one of the audit procedures as a framework but allowing more latitude. The workshop approach begins with a training exercise aimed at standardising the approach to be used, gathering the data, and reconvening to gain a consensus. Other approaches are less formalised and simply use the questionnaires. The European Business Excellence model has become a well-used general audit framework, but here we consider audits more specific to lean operations.

KOBAYASHI'S 20 KEYS

Iwao Kobayashi's concept of the "20 Keys" has gained increasing acceptance as both a manufacturing audit and an implementation guide to lean manufacturing at shop floor level. The keys relate to 20 concepts fundamental to lean operations, the majority of which are to be found in sections throughout this book. Kobayashi's concept is especially useful because

→ Guidance is given on the order of implementation of the keys

→ A five point scale is provided for each key as an aid to internal evaluation, going from level 1 beginner to level 5 ideal (certainly beyond "world class")

→ Links between the keys are established. For instance, in order to reach higher level in the production scheduling key, actions are required in all other 19 keys. It is not possible therefore to reach higher levels in most of the keys without substantial progress in all keys.

→ As an evaluation method, comparisons can be made with other organisations, although this applies to Schonberger and Fisher as well.

The sense of the 20 keys is given below showing the links to other sections in this book, and some comments on the range of characteristics required.

Note (1): For the full rating scale, from level 1 to level 5 for each key, as well as many useful tips, the full 285 page book is recommended.
Note (2): Some Western managers and critics of lean manufacturing feel that Kobayashi's ideas on operators (for instance keys 3, 4, 6, 7, 10, 15) are much too regimented and that Western workers cannot be expected to become automatons. Lean enthusiasts discount such views, saying that this represents a misunderstanding, and that standards and discipline are fundamental to continuing improvement.

1. Clean and Tidy (see section on 5S). From untidy to 100% organised, 100% of the time.
2. Participative management style (or top-down bottom-up management) (see the section on Hoshin). From disorganised to interactive, cross-functional involvement at all levels.
3. Teamworking on improvement. (See section on Continual Improvement). From low enthusiasm to highly enthusiastic and effective.

4. Overproduction, reduced inventory and reduced leadtime. (see Muda and Time Based Competitiveness). From no recognition of the waste of overproduction to mixed model production with low inventory and high customer service.

5. Changeover Reduction (see section of same title). From belief that the way to reduce total setup time is via increased batch size to full SMED

6. Continuous improvement at the workplace (see Gemba, Improvement). From haphazard to workplace improvement as the natural way of life. Kobayashi calls this "manufacturing value analysis".

7. "Zero monitoring" (see Flexible manpower lines, Cell balancing). From operators watching machines to almost no watching whilst tending several machines.

8. Process, cellular manufacturing (see Cells, Kanban). From functional organisation with push to interconnected, cellular layout with pull.

9. Maintenance (see TPM). From no maintenance or expert centred maintenance to full participative TPM.

10. Disciplined, rhythmic working (see cell balance, "repeaters"). From operators controlling breaks and one week's schedule not looking at all like another week's schedule, to synchronised breaks, with one week looking as much like the last as possible.

11. Defects (see short run SPC, pokayoke). From inspectors being responsible for defect detection, to process control, prevention, operator responsibility, and pokayoke.

12. Supplier Partnership (see Supplier Development, Supplier Associations); from adversarial, guarded to full partnership with information sharing and supply chain co-operation

13. Waste Identification and elimination (see Muda, Mapping); From no or little waste awareness to everyone "wearing muda glasses", mapping, and leading onto systematic waste elimination.

14. Worker empowerment and training (see Self Directed Work Teams). From IEs / production engineers making all improvements to workers being trained, supported, and funded to make low cost automation devices for themselves

15. Cross-functional working, multiskilling. (see BPR, Self Directed Work Teams). From job demarcation to full cross functional working and moving operators from areas of low demand to areas of high demand. Operator skill boards actively used.

16. Scheduling (see Flow, Pull, Regularity). From poor on time performance often with high inventory to excellent performance in delivery, quality, cost and schedules being achieved 100% of the time.

17. Efficiency (see Kaizen costing, open book management performance measurement). From financially oriented variance measures to balanced measures under workers own control and with information provided for decision making)

18. Technology and microprocessors. (see Point of Production control). From low operator awareness of the potential for microprocessors and automation to wide implementation through operator involvement. (NC, CNC, CAD/CAM, Electronic office,)

19. Conserving energy and materials (see Muda); from low awareness of these types of waste to full awareness

20. Appropriate Site Technology and Concurrent Engineering. (see CE). From low awareness of potential to full awareness, at middle and senior levels, including ERP, CIM, but also concurrent engineering and Taguchi methods.

According to Kobayashi, keys 1 to 4 are the basics, the starting point. These lead on to keys 5 to 20 which work together as a set. However key 4 is critical to time, key 11 to quality, and keys 6 and 19 to cost. Each of these latter 4 keys requires development in all the other keys to become fully effective. Kobayashi also uses the "bean sprout analogy" which is that, in a field of bean sprouts no one sprout can grow much ahead of the others or else it will blow down. Similarly in Lean, development must take place in all areas approximately equally.

It is interesting to note the similarity with the views of Dan Jones. Dan states that the foundation of Lean Thinking is 5S, Shop Floor Teams, 7 Quality Tools, and PDCA (keys 1, 3, 11, 6), which support production smoothing, demand smoothing, JIT, and Jidoka (keys 10, 16, 5), which in turn are held on place by waste elimination and TPM (keys 13, 9), and capped by policy deployment (key 2).

SCHONBERGER'S PRINCIPLES

Richard Schonberger, author of the excellent *Japanese Manufacturing Techniques* and *World Class Manufacturing,* has developed 16 "Principles of World Class Manufacturing". Like the 20 Keys, the 16 Principles are excellent guides to Lean Operations in themselves, and a company's progress may be measured on a 1 to 5 scale for each principle. For 16 principles this means a maximum score of 80 points with "adulthood" beginning at 53 points and "maturity" at 67 points. Once again, a rating of 4 or 5 would be fairly challenging for many manufacturers. Unlike Kobayashi, however, each principle tends to be independent of others. Perhaps surprisingly, the two evaluation systems do not cover exactly the same points although of course there is fair degree of overlap. In the section below, the Schonberger Principles are given in relation to Kobayashi with the number of the Schonberger Principle shown in brackets. A question mark indicates that the points do not exactly coincide. The detailed rating system is not given, and the reader is referred to the original.

KOBAYASHI	SCHONBERGER
Cleaning and organising	
Rationalising the system/goal alignment/Hoshin	Involve frontline staff in change and planning (2)
Team activities	Teams record and own process data (11) (?)
Reducing WIP	Cut flow time and changeover (6)
Quick changeover	Cut flow time and changeover (6)
Workplace methods and Kaizen	-
Zero monitoring	-
Cells and pull "Coupled manufacture"	(part) ".....organise by product family" (1)
Maintaining machines and equipment	-
Time control and commitment	-
Quality assurance	Reduce variation (10)
Supplier development	Best components, operators, suppliers (5)
Waste elimination	"Control root causes to cut internal transactions" (12)
Worker empowerment	"Frontliners involved in change " (4)
Cross functional working and multiskilling	"continually train for new roles" (8)
Flow scheduling	"close to customer's rate of use" (7) (?)
Efficiency control	"align performance measures with customer wants" (13)
Conserving energy and materials	-
Use of Information Systems	-
Appropriate technology	"seek simple, flexible, movable, low cost equipment in multiples" (15) and improve present capacity before buying new and before automating (15)
-	"team up with customers...." (1)
-	Use best practice information, and benchmark (2)
-	"continual, rapid improvement in what all customers want" (3)
-	Expand the variety of rewards and recognition (9)
-	"Promote/market/sell every improvement" (16)

FISHER'S SELF-TEST

Dennis Fisher, an American, has developed *The Just-in-Tine Self Test,* another self-diagnostic aid. Fisher's test comprises 68 questions all answered on a yes or no basis. The full battery of questions is only applicable to a repetitive manufacturer or to a flow shop. For a job shop or project manufacturer, some questions are not relevant. So the first step is to determine what type of manufacturer you are. One point is scored for each clear yes. For a repetitive manufacturer "Class D" is below 32 points and "Class A" above 56 points. What appears to be in Fisher's mind about an ideal operations organisation is an integration of JIT with MRPII.

The self-test is divided into

→ "Education and People" (9 questions covering management support, continuous training, organisation for JIT, management training, cross training, rewards, problem solving teams, participation in company wide problem solving, and management responsiveness to ideas.)

→ "Quality Management" (9 questions covering management support, operator responsibility for inspection, process audit established, SPC, quality at source, pokayoke, cleanliness and tidiness, source verification of incoming materials, supplier certification and rating.)

→ "Factory Flow" (9 questions covering milk round deliveries, standardised containers for delivery, delivery to point of use, deliveries pulled by processes, standardised containers used internally, build in line with daily demand, no expediting, batch sizes approaching one, and labour not kept artificially busy.)

→ "Production Processes" (11 questions covering use of cells, process support for mixed model production, manufacturing involvement in design, design for fast changeover, fixtures and tools available as needed, SMED, balanced flow (takt time?), reduction of material handling, process problem visibility (Andon?), location of manufacturing engineering (and maintenance?), preventative maintenance.)

→ Master Planning (6 questions covering level scheduling, MRP as a planning tool, management participation (in scheduling?), marketing promotes use of capacity made available by JIT, production in line with demand, near perfect on-time delivery).

→ Purchasing (7 questions covering local suppliers, single source supply, supplier rationalisation, multi-criteria supplier rating, multi-department contact points, waste elimination in purchasing, delivery lead times.)

→ Data Integrity (7 questions covering inventory accuracy, BOM accuracy, BOM structures, routing and assembly records, standards used for costing, low forecast variation, JIT accounting systems.)

→ Results (10 questions covering an operational measurement system, reduced lead times, floor space, WIP, operating expense, cost of quality and finished goods inventories; and increased productivity, inventory turns, and on-time deliveries.)

Users of the Baldridge Award or the EFQM excellence model will recognise a similar structure of enablers, processes and results. Fisher gives a page or so of text on each question. The self-tester is asked to read the material on each "no" answer and is then given reasons why this point should be done, and how to do it, at least in outline. The yes / no aspect is perhaps a little less easy to handle than the Kobayashi or Schonberger rating scale.

As a generalisation, Kobayashi is stronger on the aspects relating to management at the workplace and waste or muda. Schonberger is strongest in links with the customer, on worker involvement in continuous improvement, on design, and simplicity of process. Fisher appears strongest on links with MRPII (if that is needed!), data integrity, material handling, and on what he calls factory flow. In truth, all three have useful points to make.

FURTHER READING:

Iwao Kobayashi, *20 Keys to Workplace Improvement,* Revised Edition, Productivity Press, Portland, OR, 1995, ISBN 1-56327-109-5

Dino Petrarolo, "The 20 Keys to Workplace Improvement", *Industrial Management* (US), Jan-Feb 1998, pp 22-28

Richard Schonberger, *World Class Manufacturing: The Next Decade,* Free Press, New York, 1996, ISBN 0-684-82303-9, Chapter 2.

Dennis Fisher, *The Just-in-Time Self Test,* Irwin, Chicago, 1995, ISBN 0-7863-0299-2

David Lascelles and Roy Peacock, *Self Assessment for Business Excellence,* McGraw Hill, London, 1996

IMPROVEMENT

→ Continual Improvement
→ 5S
→ Kaikaku
→ Standards
→ String Diagrams
→ Value Engineering and Value Analysis
→ Kaizen
→ Total Productive Maintenance (TPM)
→ Overall Equipment Effectiveness (OEE)
→ Root Cause Analysis
→ Business Process Reengineering (BPR)

According to the SMMT Industry Forum, there should be three areas of focus for improvement: within a company, a company and its supplier partners, and the supply chains responsible for each major assembly. This section deals mainly with the in-company focus. However, the tools in this section can be used for the other focus areas when used with mapping tools and supplier partnership concepts.

CONTINUAL IMPROVEMENT

Continuous, or at least Continual, Improvement has become a major theme, perhaps the major theme, in manufacturing over the past 15 years and is certainly a core Lean concept. Although Kaizen has become well established since Masaaki Imai's classic work on the topic, it has become clear that there are two elements to improvement, namely continuous improvement and breakthrough improvement. Thus Juran refers to "breakthrough" activities, using "project by project" improvement, to attack "chronic" underlying quality problems as being different from more obvious problems. Davenport, in the context of business process reengineering, has referred to "the sequence of continuous alteration" between continuous improvement and more radical breakthroughs by reengineering. And Womack and Jones discuss "kaikaku" resulting in large, infrequent gains as being different from kaizen or continuous improvement resulting in frequent but small gains.

A traditional industrial engineering idea is that breakthrough or major event improvement activities are not continuous at all, but take place infrequently in response to a major change such as a new product introduction or in response to a "crisis". But during the past few years we have learned that effective breakthrough should be both proactive and frequent.

There are therefore four types of improvement, as shown in the figure. There is, or should be, a place for all four types in every organisation. Adopting lean manufacturing does not mean ignoring other forms of improvement to concentrate on kaizen and kaikaku. Passive approaches are a useful supplement and should continue. However, if all improvement is of the passive, reactive type the company may well slip behind.

Passive Incremental	Enforced Incremental
Passive Breakthrough	Enforced Breakthrough

A Classification of Improvement Types

Unfortunately, several British factories think they are doing kaizen, but their brand of kaizen is "passive" or left to chance. Improvements are left to the initiative of operators or industrial engineers or managers. If they make improvements - good. If they don't - "oh well, sometime". Passive incremental may also be termed "reactive". A reaction takes place in response to a crisis. By contrast, enforced improvement is proactive. "Crises" are actually engineered and the pressure kept on. For example, Intel brings out a new chip at regular, paced intervals and does not wait passively for technological breakthrough. 3M dictates that 30% of revenues will come from new products every year. This forces the pace.

Passive improvement has been around for many years, and it too is found in two categories - incremental and breakthrough. Classic "passive incremental" improvement approaches are the suggestion scheme and the quality circle. Passive breakthrough is classic industrial engineering or work-study, especially where such methodologies are used for factory layout, and new technology introduction.

Passive Incremental

The classic type of passive incremental improvement is the suggestion scheme, with or without rewards, and with or without team emphasis. The classic team based passive incremental improvement method is the Quality Circle. Contrary to popular conception, the reward-based suggestion scheme is alive and well at many Japanese companies. At Toyota's US plant, for instance, awards are based on points and range from $10 to $10,000. Toyota has the attitude that all suggestions are valuable, so the company is prepared to make a loss on more mundane suggestions to develop the culture of improvement. But at the other end of the Pareto, the company reckons that the top 2.5% of suggestions pay for the entire reward programme, even though a good number of suggestions at the bottom end are loss-making (taking into account the implementation time.) Thomas Edison is reported to have said that the way to have great inventions to have many inventions. Toyota also insists that all suggestions are acknowledged within 24 hours and evaluated within a week. Non-acknowledgement and non-recognition have probably been the major reason for suggestions schemes producing poor results and being abandoned.

Likewise, team based Quality Circles are an integral part of the Toyota Production System. At Toyota, QC presentations to senior management occur almost every day. At Japanese companies QCs often meet in their own time. Management involvement and support are crucial elements. Edward Lawler has described a "cycle of failure" for many Western QCs. The following sequence is typical. In early days the first circles make a big impact as pent-up ideas are released and management listens. Then the scheme is extended, usually too rapidly, to other areas. Management cannot cope with attending all these events, and is in any case often less interested. In the initial phases, the concerns of first line supervisors, who often see QCs as a threat to their authority, are not sufficiently taken care of in the rush to expand. Some supervisors may actively sabotage the scheme; others simply do not support it. Then, as time goes on, with less support from management and supervision, ideas begin to run out. The scheme fades. And it is said, "QCs are a Japanese idea which do not work in the Western culture". (By the way, it was Deming who introduced circles to Japan, albeit that Ishikawa refined the methods).

From the forgoing we lean a few important lessons; (1) not all improvements will pay, but creating the culture of improvement is more important. (2) Give it time, and expand slowly (3) recognition is important - management cannot often be expected to give personal support, so establish a facilitator who can (4) do not underestimate potential opposition, (5) react, and fast, to suggestions and (6) give them the tools and techniques, and probably the time.

PASSIVE BREAKTHROUGH

Many traditional industrial engineering and work-study projects are of the passive breakthrough type, particularly when left to the initiative of the I.E. or work-study department. Of course, IEs also work on enforced breakthrough activities initiated by management or by crisis, but passive breakthrough activities, led by IEs, have probably been the greatest source of productivity improvement this century. Many of Taiichi Ohno's activities could be classified as passive breakthrough. Apparently he was a great experimenter in the dead of night.

ENFORCED INCREMENTAL

Kaizen, as practised at Toyota, is the classic here. Waste elimination should not only be a matter of chance that relies upon operator initiative, but is driven. There are a number of ways in which this is done:

➔ Response Analysis. At Toyota operators can signal, by switch or chord, when they encounter a problem. At some workstations, there are a range of switches covering quality, maintenance, and materials shortage. When an operator activates the switch, the overhead Andon Board lights up highlighting the workstation and type of problem. People literally come running in response. But the sting is in the tail: a clock also starts running which is only stopped when the problem is resolved. These recorded times accumulate in a computer system. They are not used to apportion blame, but for analysis. Thus at the end of an appropriate period, say a fortnight, a Pareto analysis is done which reveals the most pressing problems and workstations.

➔ Line Stop. A Toyota classic, closely related to response analysis, allows operators on the line to pull a chord if a problem is encountered. Again, the Andon Board lights up. Again, the stoppage is time recorded. But the motivation to solve the problem is intense because stopping the line stops the whole plant. This means application of the 5 Whys root cause technique. (See later section).

➔ Inventory withdrawal. Many will be familiar with the classic JIT "water and rocks" analogy, whereby dropping the water level (inventory) exposes the rocks (problems). This is done with a vengeance at Toyota. Whenever there is stability, deliberate experimentation takes place by withdrawing inventory to see what will happen. Less well known is that this is a "win win" strategy: either nothing happens in which case the system runs tighter, or a "rock" is encountered which according to Toyota philosophy is a good thing. It is not any rock, but the most urgent rock. Deliberate destabilisation creates what Robert Hall has referred to as a "production laboratory".

➔ Waste Checklists. Toyota makes extensive use of waste checklists in production and non-production areas alike. A waste checklist is a set of questions, distributed to all employees in a particular area, asking them simple questions: "Do you bend to pick up a tool", "Do you walk more than 2 yards to fetch material", and so on. Where there is a positive response, there is waste. The result is that individuals and teams never run out of ideas for areas requiring improvement.

➔ The "Stage 1, Stage 2" cycle. At Toyota there is a culture that drives improvement. This culture or belief stems from the widely held attitude that each completed improvement project necessarily opens up opportunity for yet another improvement activity. For want of a better phrase, Bicheno has termed this "stage 1, stage 2" [See Cause and Effect JIT} after a list of JIT "stage 1" activities that lead to "stage 2" opportunities which in turn lead to stage 1 opportunities, and so on. The list of possible chains is very large, but an example will suffice. Thus setup reduction (stage 1) may lead to reduced buffers (stage 2), which may lead to improved layout (stage 1), leading to Improved visibility (stage 2), leading to improved quality (stage 1), leading to improved scheduling (stage 2), and so on and on.

ENFORCED BREAKTHROUGH IMPROVEMENT

Kaikaku or "Kaizen Blitz" is the subject of a separate section in this book. Kaikaku is "enforced" breakthrough. It is breakthrough because typical kaikaku events achieve between 25% and 70% improvements within either a week or within a month at most. It is enforced because the expectations and opportunities are all in place. "No" and "it can't be done" are simply not acceptable. Concentrated resources are applied.

It may be argued that Kaikaku is not "continuous" improvement. Strictly, this is correct. Yet kaikaku events can and should be repeated in the same area at regular intervals. Products change, priorities change, people change, technology improves.

Don't let the Deming PDCA cycle stand for "Please Don't Change Anything".

5S

At first glance, 5S is about good housekeeping. It is, but it goes much further. It is really about changing the mindset, about making orderly and standardised operations the norm rather than the exception. The 5 S concept is one of the cornerstones of Lean Management and has had a long association with Shingo and the Toyota Production System (where, however, it is known as the 4S system). It is fundamental to both TPM and to total quality, and has almost invariably been the first programme taken by Japanese compares in the UK when taking over operations in a British factory. 5S has a direct impact on safety, cost, quality, delivery, and on OEE

The 5 S's stem from 5 Japanese words. It is a name that has stuck, despite the fact that few English speakers understand the Japanese words. There have been a number of attempts to use English words whilst retaining the five S's; for example the Shingo version refers to Sort, Straighten, Shine, Systematise, Sustain. However, these are generally unsatisfactory. We have adopted a Western version, origin unknown, called CANDO whilst still referring to the concept as "5S". Toyota, by the way, uses "4S" combining A and N below. There is also "6S" adding Safety.

C IS FOR CLEANUP. This is about removing all items (especially accumulated dirt and grime, but also inventory, paper, furniture, tools, memos, manuals, rubbish, filing cabinets, etc) that are not required or are unnecessary within a period ahead. Such items are waste, or lead to waste. They take up space, lead to extra walking around, and lead to waste of time whilst searching for needed items buried under piles of less important material. An office example is the "clean desk" policy run by several companies, requiring employees to have a clear desk at the end of each day. In the office beware of paperwork that is shuffled, reread, and searched through often several times per day. It's all waste. Cleanout also includes fixing: any tools or equipment that is broken or not calibrated must either be thrown away or repaired - decide which, and act.

There are two approaches. One is to begin with a longer period (say 6 months) and to clear all that is not foreseen to be used within that period; then to reduce the period until you are working with only (say) this week's items. The more common approach is to "red tag" items that are not in use or where there is uncertainty. Dates are written on the red tags. Tagged items are then removed and either thrown out or, where there is uncertainty about the future use of the item, placed in a holding area. Tagged items remaining in the holding area for more than say 6 months are thrown out. Red tagging is best done by in focused areas, one at a time. "Blitz" one area, then move on. Red tagging should also be done by both operators from the area, who should be issued with say 4 red tags and challenged to use them up, and by red tag pairs comprising a supervisor from the area and an outsider. Cleanup is also an opportunity to review the floor paint layout and policy. Are the aisles in the right place bearing in mind the requirements for flow, are the colours used appropriate, and so forth. Finally don't forget to include windows, walls (are those posters still appropriate?), lighting, and the overhead beams and roof.

A IS FOR ARRANGING; "a place for everything". This step aims to arrange the workplace and it's associated tools, equipment and inventory in the optimal locations. The analogy between the kitchen and the garage is often used. In the kitchen, cutlery is kept in specific slots in a specific drawer; in the garage tools, rags, and half used tins of paint often lie around for ages. The goal is to make the workplace not only good and easy to work in, but also that anyone should be able to locate the necessary equipment. Reaching, bending and walking should be minimised.   It is really about having things easy to hand, labelled, classified, and easily visible. Time wasted should be cut by careful location of tools and materials. Do a Pareto in order to locate the most frequently used items closest. It may be possible to incorporate some failsafing: cords attached to tools, racking or slots that do not hold other than the correct tool.

Instructions and standards should be clear (drawings better than words), up to date, and be located at the workplace. Shadow boards may be used for tools, books arranged by topic, shelves not too high, wheels on carts, heavy low and light high, colour coded connections and pipes, and so on. It is also about inventory: having specific locations or footprints for specific parts, perhaps painted squares, minimum and maximum quantities shown, and of course a limit on excessive parts delivered lineside too early. When combined with cleanup, this lays the foundation for the kanban system. Taking arrangement further means thinking about overhead "Andon" boards, signalling systems, progress boards, charts and graphs, and establishing responsibility for them being kept up to date. A major consideration should be consideration of the correct size for pallets and boxes, and the arrangements for their movement so as to avoid double handling.

N IS FOR NEATNESS; "everything in its place" and ready to go. The simple fact is that the cleaner or tidier a location is, the easier it is to see if something is out of place. Once again, the garage analogy; with clean garage an oil leek is seen straight away. Neatness has a direct impact on productivity: searching for lost papers and tools should be eliminated. It is also a safety issue. Responsibility for Neatness should lie with the operator, not with cleaners. Good 5S programmes establish what are termed "5 Minute Cleanup" routines. Here, each operator develops his or her own 5 minute per day clean and check routine, for each day of the week. Note that this is not left to chance; it is a carefully timed and documented set of actions that are to be undertaken on specific days of the week. The documentation, of course, should be kept at the workplace and should for instance specify what abnormality looks like and what cleaning agents should be used. Neatness and cleanliness extends to non-seen areas: machines need to be clean inside and out - in fact, making the innards of machines visible by using transparent covers is desirable. Routine maintenance may be incorporated: oil every day, replace after 5000 sheets, and "aircraft style checks" where items are checked at the start of every shift (have you ever been into a bank to discover a non-working pen chained to the counter?). One important activity is identifying which maintenance activities are the responsibility of the ordinary staff, and which are the responsibilities of specialist maintenance staff. Responsibility for the photocopier is good example; clearly define who is responsible for what: secretaries, staff, specialists.

D IS FOR "DISCIPLINE". This step aims to keep the factory or office in a "Chief Executive's visit" state all the time. The thought here is that it is easier to keep things going, than to stop and restart over again - like the momentum of a train. This is not discipline in the army sense, but rather getting into the routine or mindset of keeping up the standards and procedures established in earlier steps. The difficulty of achieving this should not be underestimated; Toyota reckons it takes several months to establish this with a new employee.

So what is required to keep up the momentum? First, a regular audit. It is a good idea to establish a 5S committee of operators themselves and get them to establish the audit checklist. But remember to include the not-so-obvious: clothing, corners, waste bins, stairways, windows, signs, electrical connections, as well as the obvious machines, jigs, and stores. The audit time should be at random intervals. The audit checklist should not be used only as weekly pat on the back, but as a means of detecting any deterioration, and the reasons for that deterioration. But rewards and recognition, both intrinsic and extrinsic, are also part of the game. Intrinsic rewards include recognition of good work, perhaps by a weekly "floating trophy" and built into staff evaluations, and extrinsic rewards may include small prizes or vouchers. Much would depend on company culture.

Finally, **O STANDS FOR ONGOING IMPROVEMENT.** This is maintaining the tempo of continuous improvement. Here we should not only be concerned with cleaning up spillage of oil and so forth, but asking why the spillage occurred in the first place. Get to the root cause. This is Juran's views on "chronic" and "sporadic" defects; whilst it is OK to tackle sporadic defects by fire fighting, an attack on the underlying and continuing sources of defects means that the effects go on and on and on. How do we move towards this? First, by establishing clear standards so one can move from standard to standard. Second, by a continuing Pareto attack on the recurring sources of problems, which means having records to do this. Third, by tightening the red tag horizon. Fourth, by seeking pokayoke in regard to housekeeping; for example machines that will not start before routine checks have been made or audible warnings that activate if bar codes are not scanned. And we also need to repeat the Cleanup activity at regular intervals because products and tooling changes. Most of all we need to encourage a questioning culture combined with visibility - so that if something is out of place or missing it is not only noticed, but also questioned. This takes years of management persistence.

KAIKAKU

Kaikaku or "instant revolution" is one of the most exciting concepts to emerge in recent years. Unlike many "fads" kaikaku delivers the results in a very short space of time. Literally within one week a company could be benefiting from a leap in productivity in one area of your plant or office.

Kaikaku is about "going for it", about doing not planning, about a preference for doing it now and reasonably rather than later (but perhaps never) even though it may be done better, about learning by doing, by trial and error. It is also about involvement on the shop floor by shop floor people. It is about real empowerment to just do it without asking for permission to make every little change. Flow, especially one-piece flow, is often the aim and the event.

Kaikaku aims at spectacular and very rapid productivity improvement in a focused area. As Imai has pointed out, it is often easier to achieve a 20% improvement than a 5% improvement! Kaikaku exercises have gained the serious attention of managers in the last few years, if for no other reason than the scale of the gains achieved. Today, Kaikaku, or "Kaizen Blitz" (the name used by the US Association for Manufacturing Excellence) has been proven in both service and manufacturing companies, where management has been brave enough to take the challenge. Not surprisingly the concept has its origins in the Toyota Production System, and is based on Taiichi Ohno's Seven Wastes or "Muda", on "5S", and on the "5 Whys" questioning culture. It is a no-holds-barred, go-for-it approach and the exact opposite of "paralysis-by-analysis".

Kaikaku is often used to target the "low hanging fruit" in a company, but may also be used as part of a programme of ongoing improvement.

Although the concept has been around for at least 15 years, kaikaku has had a surprisingly modest number of customers, at least until recently. Probably three things have now got if off the ground: the work of the Kaizen Institute (through their founder Imai) who adopts kaikaku in typically week-long workshops but calls it kaizen, the work of Association for Manufacturing Excellence in the US which championed what they refer to as "kaizen blitz", and the publication of Womack and Jones' book "Lean Thinking" which described kaikaku in action at several companies, including the classic Porsche story where the kaikaku experts began by asking "where is the factory?" Because "this is obviously the warehouse", and proceeded to get the once-staid and be-suited "Doctor Engineers" to walk around the plant with a power saw cutting off all racking above waist height so as to improve visibility. That story gives the flavour of a kaikaku event.

Kaikaku should be seen as alternating with continuous improvement activities. Professor Dan Jones argues that kaikaku is not a one-off event but that subsequent kaikaku will continue to yield dramatic breakthrough results. This sequence of alternating between kaikaku and continuous improvement is not unique to JIT nor is it new.

There are several variations to kaikaku events. For instance, one version uses engineers and managers (including from the outside) to work with the shop floor staff. Another version leaves it pretty well to the operators themselves, working under a facilitator.

> "Whether you believe you can,
> or whether you believe you can't,
> you're absolutely right."
>
> HENRY FORD

A BRIEF OVERVIEW OF A TYPICAL KAIKAKU EVENT (BASED ON AN ACTUAL EVENT)

Following a mapping exercise at an automotive part supplier it was decided to stage a 1+2+2-day series of kaikaku events. Initial mapping had revealed a large proportion of movement wastes and double handling, and apparently large inventories.

The findings of the original mapping exercise were presented to a group of senior and middle managers who decided that 1+2+2 type event would be most suitable for their situation which included a relatively low awareness level of JIT / Lean Manufacturing / Waste concepts, fairly complex product routings, and a number of machines that were fixed to the floor. The target area for the exercise was identified as being one where there appeared not only to be good opportunity, but where the product range was limited to a family of products with similar routings.

The team to carry out the event was identified. It comprised the external facilitator, the kaizen facilitator from the company, the cell supervisor, an industrial engineer from another site in the same group, an accountant from the factory, and three cell operators. All had to commit to being completely free of other duties for the duration of the events, although the industrial engineer and accountant were permitted to attend half-hour morning meetings.

DAY 1

The first day, or half day, to be precise, included an introduction to lean manufacturing concepts. This was done by playing a JIT / Lean game. The 7 wastes were identified and talked through, and the desirable aims established: improve flow by reducing batch size (one-piece flow would not be possible), reducing waste, and encouraging flow. An outline of the forthcoming event was also given. A degree of team building was also the aim at this stage.

DAYS 2 AND 3

The first two-day event began the following week. After an initial briefing the team split into three sub-teams, each tasked to complete their study by the end of the first morning. The three cell operators were each involved in a different initial analysis team. The layout team made a cut-out model of the cell and adjacent areas during the first morning, and measured total distances moved. The inventory and material handling team quickly got into questioning the amount of parts stored in the cell (several weeks supply in some cases), and the material movement quantities and methods. The process team chose to get into the ergonomics of the workstations and assembly methods that were the apparent cause of some quality problems. Data collection included measuring inventory, estimating lead times, timing of selected activities (some in greater detail than others), measurement of flow length, and taking photographs.

Immediately after lunch the sub-teams each made a brief presentation to fellow team members. Brainstorming and prioritising took place during the first afternoon. The team spent a good part of the first afternoon at the cell, discussing alternatives in situ. Some immediate changes were decided upon and a number of airlines and electrical connection points were moved overnight. During the second day, the changes that were actually implemented included: relocation of a small press, the swapping around of a bicycle shed and a storage area, the relocation of a material store in the cell enabling a smoother flow to take place, changes to the assembly process itself, the repair of a door which was causing a draft, a drastic reduction of batch quantities (changeover was already very short), and, as a result, new material handling procedures. Interestingly, some of the women cell operators were initially opposed to any change on the basis of safety, but became enthusiastic supporters when changes proposed by their fellow operators were put in place. The afternoon of the third day was spent prioritising actions, and assigning responsibilities. The list ran to several pages.

Days 4 and 5

During the intervening period, alterations to some work desks were made by maintenance, racks were acquired (from another part of the plant), preparations to move a machine were made, and a variety of materials (e.g. paint), signs, and tools were acquired. Briefings were also given to senior management. The operators who had participated in the initial days were encouraged to discuss what had happened and what was planned with their work mates.

On days 4 and 5 the agreed upon changes were made. The major change was to layout, including the relocation of a semi-automated assembly machine. New material handling arrangements were begun. Then the line was run and observed. Some further changes were necessary. A number of new ideas emerged; some of which were immediately attempted. During day 5, after further adjustment, the team attempted to write new standards. These could not be completed. In any case all the operators were to be involved, not just the three operators on the kaikaku team.
An estimate of the savings in space, inventory, throughput time, material handling, were made, and "before and after" photographs assembled.

On day 5, one of the women operators commented, "I have been in this company for 15 years, and I have seen more change during the last two weeks than I saw during all those years put together." Another commented, "Now I have seen the new system, I really don't know how we managed previously."

Further reading:
Sid Joynson and Andrew Forrester, *Sid's Heroes: 30% Improvement in Productivity in 2 Days*, BBC, London, 1996
Edward E Lawler III, *From the Ground Up: Six Principles for Building the New Logic Organisation*, Jossey-Bass, San Francisco, 1996, Chapter 6
Anthony C Laraia, Patricia Moody, and Robert Hall, *The Kaizen Blitz: Accelerating Breakthroughs in Productivity and Performance*, John Wiley and Sons, New York, 1999

Magazine:
The best magazine / journal on "kaizen blitz" is *Target: The Periodical of the Association for Manufacturing Excellence*.
Fax AME at 001 847 520 0163.   (I.e. a USA fax number) Highly recommended.

STANDARDS

Standards are the basis for quality and continuous improvement. They make lean manufacturing possible. Standardisation allows you to "hold the gains", as Juran would say, rather than slip back to old ways. Standards should cover three aspects: work time, work sequence, and standard work-in-process. All are necessary. On work time, both takt time and current cycle time (i.e. the time taken for one cycle of the process) should be recorded.

At the outset it should be said that by "standards" is not meant the rigid, work-study imposed, job specification that is associated with classic mass production. Such standards have no place in the world of lean. For such "jobs" industrial sabotage and absenteeism are to be expected. Conversely, what is also not being discussed is the human-relations based reaction against these job standards, which are supposed to enrich jobs, but lead to no standards, which in turn lead to decreased safety and productivity. Standardisation has become unglamorous and unfashionable, with the possible exception of ISO9000. Work standards are frequently considered to be something that applies to operators, but not to managers.

Despite what some people think about Frederick Taylor, there remains "one best way", with available technology, to do any task which will minimise time and effort, and maximise safety, quality and productivity. To some this may sound like boring repetition, but the "new" standards are about participation in developing the best and safest way, mastery of several jobs, and the ability to adapt to changes in rate and mix in the short term.

Ohno realised that the achievement of standardised work, with minimum variance, was the essential ingredient to allow one piece flow and JIT production. Deming, in proposing the PDCA cycle, saw improvement moving from standard to standard. Juran emphasised the importance of "holding the gains" by establishing standards following a process improvement, rather than allowing them to drift back to the old ways. Recently the "Learning Organisation" has become fashionable, including "knowledge harvesting" from everyone in the organisation. How is this to be achieved? By documenting experience; in other words by establishing standards from which others may learn.

When standardising work, the same procedure adopted for scheduling should be used. That is, list the activities and sort out the frequently repeating activities from the irregular activities. Standardise the repeaters, but then try to "standardise" the irregular activities into blocks. For instance, meet with supervisors and fetch parts at regular times, not random times.

At Toyota, emphasis is placed on workers documenting their own standards, and in mastering both a wider range of work tasks and greater responsibility for supporting tasks. Operators themselves establish work cycles within the specified takt time. It may be that they are assisted in this task by industrial engineers and supervisors, but the operators must write up the final documentation of work standards themselves. This achieves four goals. First, there can be no question that work standards are not understood. Second, the operator is forced to think about the best way in which he or she should do the work within the takt time. A trained operator will frequently do a better job than an uninvolved work study officer. Third, the responsibility for setting the standard and then maintaining it is clearly up to the operator. There is motivation to update the standard when improved ways are found. And, fourth, because the standards reflect what actually happens rather than what might happen, learning can take place particularly when operators change jobs. In other words this is job enrichment and job mastery.

Lawler has pointed out that for job enrichment to succeed requires a new form of organisation, with emphasis on process rather than on function. So standards work best where there are cells or teams, where operators are responsible for productivity and quality of the whole area or process.

Too many operations-based organisations delude themselves on standards. It is tempting to simply impose work standards by getting industrial engineers or work study people to do the work and to post standards at workstations, or worse to keep them in a file. Then of course, there is no buy-in, no foundation for continuous improvement, and worst of all a great likelihood of large process variance. So the quick way turns out to be the least effective way and often a total waste. Traditional "Taylorism", is suitable only in the sweat shop. The Toyota way takes time to train operators to do the analysis and standardisation themselves - they need to not only learn basic work-study principles but also to appreciate the reasons why they should do it. Toyota regards work standardisation as one of its most challenging management tasks. Robert Hall believes that this worker-oriented standardisation, requiring high levels of operator skill and motivation, is one of the main limitations to the growth of Toyota.

So what should a standard contain? Operator standards should contain the takt time, the detailed work sequence steps that are involved together with the time taken for each step (these should be written in the operators own words), and the standard inventory quantity or kanban quantity involved during the takt time cycle. These should be supported by a diagram of the operator movements, possibly a sketch of any operation requiring clarification, any tools that are used, any quality checks, and a note on any special operation that is required to be carried out periodically. Standard procedures can be colour coded to match the product that carries a label of matching colour. When an engineering change occurs, a number on the product should match the number on the standard sheet. Often, a standard should cover not only what to do when things are normal, but also what to do if things go wrong. Consider health and safety. There must be own responsibility for the standard, for publishing it, for keeping it at the workplace, and for keeping it up to date. At Intel where consistency is an absolute requirement, operators audit one another using the standard instructions.

When cellular manufacturing is established or when takt times change, operators in the cell are encouraged to rebalance the line themselves or to change their own work standards to the new takt time. In this case there may be work standard for the whole cell, including a diagram showing the movements of each operator.

Managers and other workers should also consider documenting their standards. At least there should be broad standards for repetitive activities such as meetings, the budget cycle, personnel procedures, document preparation, placing of orders, appraisals, and so forth. The broad steps or a loose descriptive format may be appropriate. The same PDCA thoughts apply; if new form of meeting is found to work better than the old one, document both with comments on why the new works better. But do it, otherwise the opportunity to learn may be lost.

Robert Hall has pointed out that there are three stages of standardisation. The first is "outcome only" where the standard is established in a plan or drawing but how to get there is not specified. This generally leads to a high level of variation, and the need for inspectors. The second stage is "standardised processes" where variance is reduced by following standardised methods to achieve the outcome, supported in good cases by for instance SPC and pokayoke. The third stage is "standardised predictive methods" whereby a high level of consistency is achieved directly from the design by using standardised processes that work first time "without the need to prototype, test, or make special tools". Very few companies or processes are at this stage.

FURTHER READING:
Robert W Hall, "Standard Work: Holding the Gains", *Target,* Fourth Quarter, 1998, pp 13- 19
Taiichi Ohno, *Toyota Production System,* Productivity Press, Portland, OR, 1988
Edward E Lawler III, *From the Ground Up: Six Principles for Building the New Logic Organisation,* Jossey-Bass, San Francisco, 1996, Chapter 6

String Diagrams for Products, People, and Vehicles.

The string diagram is one of the industrial engineer's oldest tools, but still has application today. Use them regularly not just for product flows and material handling, but also for the movement of people around a cell, in changeover and in maintenance.

Begin with a scale diagram of the plant on a pin board. Select out a few major products, and trace their movement around the factory, showing the flowpath by means of coloured string and drawing pins. Then question, simplify, and quantify. The power of such a tool is its visual impact. For cost effectiveness, the string diagram is hard to beat.

On separate diagrams, trace the movements of operators doing regular work, doing changeover operations, and routine maintenance. Strangely, although material flows are often studied in detail, operator movements are sometimes ignored. What is the total distance moved to do a changeover? How many times does the operator go to and from a tool rack or walk around a machine during a changeover?

Vehicle movements can also be traced. Several studies have shown that the human eye and judgement is almost as effective as sophisticated routing algorithms, in sorting out shortest routes, provided there is a map showing the required visits.

So simple. So effective.

Value Engineering and Value Analysis

Value engineering and analysis (VE/VA) has traditionally been used for cost reduction in engineering design. But the power of its methodology means that it is an effective weapon for quality and productivity improvement in manufacturing and in services. Today the term value management (VM) recognises this fact.

The first step in any VA/VE/VM project is Orientation. This involves selecting the appropriate team, and training them in basic value concepts. The best VE/VA/VM is done in multidisciplinary teams. "Half of VE is done by providing the relevant information," says Jaganathan. By this he means that clarity of communication about customer (internal or external) is half the battle, particularly if customer needs have changed without anyone taking notice.

VM proper begins by systematically identifying the most important functions of a product or service. Then alternatives for the way the function can be undertaken are examined using creative thinking. A search procedure homes in on the most promising alternatives, and eventually the best alternative is implemented. One can recognise in these steps much similarity with various other quality techniques such as quality function deployment, the systematic use of the 7 tools of quality, and the Deming cycle. In fact these are all mutually reinforcing. VM brings added insight, and a powerful analytical and creative force to bear.

Value engineering was pioneered in the USA by General Electric, but has gained from value specialists such as Mudge and from the writers on creative thinking such as Edward de Bono. Today the concepts of TRIZ are most relevant (see separate section). The Society of American Value Engineers (SAVE) has fostered the development.

VM usually works at the fairly detailed level of a particular component or sub-system, but has also been used in a hierarchical fashion working down level by level from an overall product or service concept to the detail. At each level the procedure described would be repeated. Like many other quality and productivity techniques, VM is a group activity. It requires a knowledgeable group of people, sharing their insights and stimulating one another's ideas, to make progress. But there is no limitation on who can participate. VM can and has been used at every level from chief executive to shop floor.

What appears to give value management particular power is the deliberate movement from "left brain" (linear) analysis to "right brain" (creative) thinking. (Stringer has explained this.) Effective problem solving requires both the logical step forward and the "illogical" creative leap. Edward de Bono, of lateral thinking fame, talks about "provolution" - faster than evolution but more controlled than revolution.

VALUE ENGINEERING and ANALYSIS
(VE and VA)

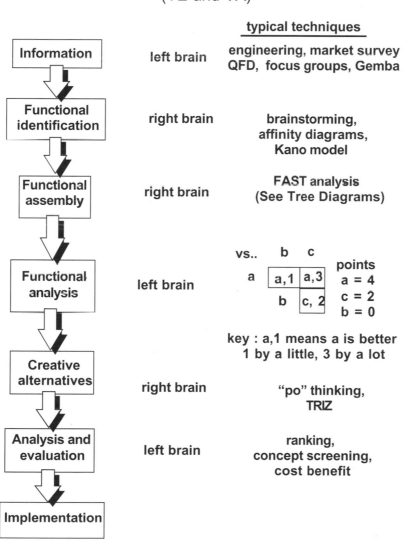

		typical techniques
Information	left brain	engineering, market survey QFD, focus groups, Gemba
Functional identification	right brain	brainstorming, affinity diagrams, Kano model
Functional assembly	right brain	FAST analysis (See Tree Diagrams)
Functional analysis	left brain	
Creative alternatives	right brain	"po" thinking, TRIZ
Analysis and evaluation	left brain	ranking, concept screening, cost benefit
Implementation		

vs.. b c
a | a,1 | a,3 |
b | | c, 2 |

points
a = 4
c = 2
b = 0

key : a,1 means a is better
1 by a little, 3 by a lot

FUNCTIONAL ANALYSIS

Functional analysis is the first step. The basic functions or customer requirements of the product or service are listed, or brainstormed out. (Right brain thinking.) A function is best described by a verb and a noun, such as "make sound", "transfer pressure", "record personal details" or "greet customer". The question to be answered is "what functions does this product/service undertake?"

Typically there will be a list of half a dozen or more functions. There is a temptation to take the basic function for granted. Do not do this; working through often gives very valuable insights. For instance, for a domestic heating time controller, some possible functions are "activate at required times", "encourage economy", and "supply heat when needed". The example shows a hamburger design.

Pairwise comparison or points distribution may be used to weight the functions or requirements. In pairwise comparison, each function is compared with each other function, and 1 point is given to the most important of the two, or zero points if the functions are considered equally important. Adding up the scores gives the relative weightings These relative weightings need to be converted to percentages such that the sum adds up to 100%. Now the components of the product are listed as columns in the matrix. See the figure. Then the importance of each component to each function is estimated and converted to a percentage of total cost. In the example, the function "taste good" is estimated to be influenced 50% by the beef and 25% each by bun and ketchup. The influence is written in the bottom left hand corner of each cell. The weighted influence (i.e. the weight x the influence) is written in the top right of each cell. The overall influence of each component is the sum of the top right hand cell entries, and is written in a row below the matrix. Then the cost of each component is estimated, and written in a row. The last step is to calculate a value index, which is the influence % divided by the cost %. Ratios less than one are prime candidates for cost reduction. Ratios substantially greater than one indicate the possibility of enhancing the feature. Back to the right brain.

Matrix Analysis for VE/VA

customer requirements	importance	percentage importance	components			
			beef	bun	lettuce	ketchup
taste good	6	4 6	.5 2 3	.25 11.5		.25 11.5
provide nutrition	2	1 5	.7 10.5	.3 4.5		
appeal visually	1	8	.3 2.4	.2 1.6	.3 2.4	.2 1.6
value for money	4	3 1	.5 15.5	.5 15.5		
		100%				
overall influence		%	51.4	33.1	2.4	13.1
cost (%)		%	6 2	3 0	2 0	8
value index		influence/ cost	0.83	1.1	0.12	1.6
			reduce cost ?	OK	reduce cost !	enhance

CREATIVITY

Now the creative phase begins. This is concerned with developing alternative, more cost effective, ways of achieving the basic functions and reducing costs of the most important components. Here the rules of brainstorming must be allowed - no criticism, listing down all ideas, writing down as many ideas as possible however apparently ridiculous. Various "tricks" can be used; deliberate short periods of silence, writing ideas on cards anonymously, sequencing suggestions in a "round robin" fashion, making a sketch, role-playing out a typical event, viewing the scene from an imaginary helicopter or explaining the product to an "extra terrestrial". Humour can be an important part of creativity.

A particularly powerful tool is the use of the de Bono "po" word. This is simply a random noun selected from a dictionary to conjure up mental images that are then used to develop new ideas. For instance "cloud" could be used in conjunction with the design of packaging where the basic function was "give protection". The word cloud conjures images of fluffiness (padding?), air (air pockets?), rain (waterproof?), silver lining (metal reinforcement?), shadow (can't see the light, leads to giving the user information), cloud is "hard to pick up" (how is the packaging lifted?), wind (whistling leading to a warning of overload?), moisture (water/humidity resistant? water can take the shape of its container - can the packaging?), obscuring the view (a look inside panel?), and so on. Do not jump to other "po" words; select one and let the group exhaust its possibilities.

ANALYSIS AND EVALUATION

Now back to the left brain. Sometimes a really outstanding idea will emerge. Otherwise there may be several candidates. Some of these candidates may need further investigation before they can be recommended. (In the above example, is it feasible or possible to introduce some sort of metal reinforcement?). Beware of throwing out ideas too early - the best ideas are often a development from an apparently poor idea. So take time to discuss them. In some cases it may be necessary for the team to take a break while more technical feasibility is evaluated or costs determined, by specialists.

There are several ways to evaluate. Pairwise comparison with multi-discipline group discussion is good possibility. Another possibility is to write all ideas on cards, then give a set of cards to pairs of group members, and ask each pair to come up with the best two ideas. Then get the full group to discuss all the leading ideas. Yet another is to draw up a cost-benefit chart (cost along one axis, benefits along another). Ask the group members to plot the locations of ideas on the chart. There is no reason why several of these methods cannot be used together. Do what makes the group happy - it is their project and their ideas.

IMPLEMENTATION

Implementation of the most favourable change is the last step. One of the benefits of the VM process is that group members tend to identify with the final solution, and to understand the reasons behind it. This should make implementation easier and faster.

FURTHER READING:

Kaneo Akiyama, *Function Analysis,* Productivity Press, Cambridge MA, 1991, ISBN 0-915299-81-X

G. Jaganathan, *Getting More at Less Cost,* Tata McGraw Hill, New Delhi, 1996, ISBN 0-07-460166-0

ACKNOWLEDGEMENT:

Many of the original ideas on value engineering are due to Art Mudge. These and other ideas have been further developed by Dick Stringer and Graham Bodman of the South African Value Management Foundation.

KAIZEN

Kaizen is the Japanese name for continuous improvement. As such it is central to Lean operations. It brings together several of the tools and techniques described in this book plus a few besides. The word originates from Maasaki Imai who wrote a book of the same name and made Kaizen popular in the West. Although a registered name of the Kaizen Institute, the word is now widely used and understood and has appeared in the English dictionary.

According to Imai, Kaizen comprises several elements. Kaizen is both a philosophy and a set of tools.

THE PHILOSOPHY OF KAIZEN – Quality begins with the customer. But customers' views are continuously changing and standards are rising, so continuous improvement is required. Kaizen is dedicated to continuous improvement, in small increments, at all levels, forever (!). Everyone has a role, from top management to shop floor employees. Top management must allocate the resources and establish the strategy, systems, procedures and organisational structures necessary for Kaizen to work. Middle managers are responsible for implementing Kaizen. They must monitor performance of the continuous improvement programme, and ensure that employees are educated in the use of the necessary tools. Supervisors are responsible for applying Kaizen. They must maintain the rate of suggestions, coach, and improve communications at the workplace. And shop-floor employees must make suggestions, learn new jobs, use the tools, and generally participate in continuous improvement activities individually and in teams. Imai's book has several examples of how this philosophy is works its way down the organisational hierarchy in Japanese companies.

John Shook, speaking at the Lean Summit 1998, made the point that there are two types of kaizen, Flow Kaizen and Process Kaizen. Flow Kaizen is about value stream improvement, getting flow going, and should be a major concern of senior management. Process Kaizen is about the elimination of waste, which should be more the responsibility of the front line. Each level in an organisation has a responsibility for both, but the emphasis changes.

Imai believes that without active attention, the gains made will simply deteriorate (like the engineers' concept of entropy). But Imai goes further. Unlike Juran who emphasises "holding the gains", Kaizen involves building on the gains by continuing experimentation and innovation.

According to Imai there are several guiding principles. These include:

→ Questioning the rules (standards are necessary but work rules are there to be broken and must be broken with time)

→ Developing resourcefulness (it is a management priority to develop the resourcefulness and participation of everyone)

→ Try to get to the Root Cause (try not to solve problems superficially)

→ Eliminate the whole task (question whether a task is necessary; in this respect Kaizen is similar to BPR),

→ Reduce or change activities (be aware of opportunities to combine tasks).

THE TOOLS OF KAIZEN – Kaizen incorporates several tools but the most well known are the Deming Cycle, "5 S", the "5 M Checklist", and the 5 Whys. Also central to Kaizen is the recognition and elimination of waste or Muda (see the section on the Wastes). 5 S and the 5 Whys are described in a separate sections. Visual management is a feature; making operations and quality visible through charts, displayed schedules, kanban, painted designated inventory and tool locations, and the like.

Standards are important in kaizen, to prevent slipping back to old ways. The Kaizen Institute believes there should be periods of consolidation to allow new ways to bed-in, rather than rushing ahead. This idea is absolutely compatible with Deming's "Standardise, Plan, Do, Check" sequence, or Juran's "holding the gains". Standards and Learning are inter-linked. The Joy Manufacturing Company, for instance, communicates value engineering improvements to sites around the world. At Toyota, engineers on new product development make extensive use of checklists. When an engineer learns something new, that knowledge is added to a checklist used for all future vehicles.

Recently, Imai has extended and elaborated on Kaizen in Gemba Kaizen. The Gemba concept is discussed in a separate section.

Kate Mackle of the British Kaizen Institute promotes Kaizen through a bottom-up learning process, which eventually permeates the whole organisation. For this a good champion is needed, and the Institute has developed a methodology for identifying suitable people.

Yuso Yasuda has described the Toyota suggestion scheme or "Kaizen system". The scheme is co-ordinated by a "creative idea suggestion committee" whose chairmanship has included Toyota chairmen (Toyoda and Saito) as well as Taiichi Ohno. Rewards for suggestions are given at Toyota based on a points system. Points are scored for tangible and intangible benefits, and for adaptability, creativity, originality, and effort. The rewards are invariably small amounts, and are not based on a percentage of savings. However operators value the token reward and the presentation ceremony itself. Note the contrast with typical Western Suggestion Schemes. Toyota recognises that all suggestions or kaizen ideas may not be beneficial. The Pareto law certainly applies. There will be many ideas that are not really worthwhile, but at the other end of the distribution there will be few hugely beneficial ideas which make the whole scheme very worthwhile. One is reminded of the classic statement about advertising, "I waste half of the money I spend but the problem is I don't know which half".

FURTHER READING:
Maasaki Imai, *Kaizen: The Key to Japan's Competitive Success*, McGraw Hill, New York, 1986
Maasaki Imai, *Gemba Kaizen*, McGraw Hill, New York, 1997
Yuasa Yasuda, *40 Years, 20 Million Ideas*, Productivity Press, Cambridge MA, 1991, ISBN 0-915299-74-7

The Kaizen Institute (UK), 4 Tavistock Place, London WC1H 9RA Tel 0171 713 0407

Total Productive Maintenance (TPM)

TPM aims at zero breakdowns, but it also aims at zero defects. TPM evolved out of Preventive Maintenance (PM), and has much in common with Total Quality. PM was an activity centred in the specialist maintenance function (concerned with maintenance records and information, the prediction of the failure or "bathtub" curve, condition monitoring, and with optimal maintenance timing decisions). TPM includes these but goes far wider by recognising that everyone has a role to play. As with John Oakland's TQM model, TPM requires underlying Culture, Commitment, and Communication, working in Systems, with Tools, and by Teams. In TQM we talk about the "chain of quality"; the TPM equivalent is the equipment life cycle. In TPM, we extend the boundary of consideration from the machine itself to include the operator, the product, the process, and the environment. And, centrally, both TQM and TPM aim at prevention. (In TQM prevention not detection of defects, in TPM prevention of breakdowns, not reacting to problems.) Finally, another similarity is that both TPM and TQM aim to "spread the load": there are just not sufficient qualified maintenance / quality specialists around, so they are best used in training, in facilitating, and in tackling the most difficult maintenance / quality problems, and not in routine work especially routine work in areas where others have greater familiarity.

In common with JIT, TPM attempts to make maintenance and problems visible, not buried away in a computer system. It also uses the JIT credo of "management by fact".

Why "productive"? Because one wishes to gain productivity, not merely maintain. TPM like TQM has been one of the great ventures during the last decade, but has been of lower prominence than TQM. There is also much in common between JIT and TPM: both rely on the thinking worker, both aim at waste reduction, and both emphasise simplicity and visibility.

Today, TPM encompasses energy management, safety, education and training, and should include a form of Hoshin Management (see separate section) whereby objectives are communicated and discussed throughout the organisation.

There are some central concepts of TPM, some of which we met elsewhere in this publication: In brief they are:

5S. The 5 S concept is the place to start with TPM. In this book, we have preferred to use the acronym CANDO rather than the Japanese S's. 5 S is a complete section in this publication. Let us just emphasise here that 5 S has a hidden agenda no less important than the 5 S's themselves: it aims at pride in the workplace. It aims to shift traditional thinking away from "maintenance is someone else's responsibility" towards "it's everyone's business, every day".

The "Six Big Losses". These are

1. Breakdown losses: the most serious type of loss; to be avoided

2. Setup and adjustment losses (delaying the start of work)

3. Idling and minor stoppages (due to necessary minor adjustments)

4. Reduced speed losses (unable to run at full speed)

5. Start-up losses (pre-production breakdowns)

6. Quality defects (as a result of imperfect equipment), and Yield losses.

The six big losses have different causes and different solutions, so you need to know where you are. This means measuring each one. All items of equipment, but especially bottlenecks, should be analysed and the losses categorised. This is the first step to improvement. Inevitably you will find a Pareto (80/20) distribution, so concentrate on the vital few.

OEE (OVERALL EQUIPMENT EFFECTIVENESS) – An effective way to measure availability and TPM performance is through OEE. OEE is closely related to the 6 Big Losses. See the next section.

"AT ITS WORST WHEN NEW" – This provocative statement goes to the heart of TPM. Why should an item of equipment be at its worst when new? Because, it may not yet be quality capable, standard procedures not yet worked out, failsafing (pokayoke) devices not yet added, operating and failure modes not yet known, 6 big losses not yet measured or understood, and vital internal elements not yet made visible (through transparent covers) or monitored by condition monitoring.

VISIBILITY – Like JIT, TPM aims to make what is happening clear for all to see. This means maintenance records need to be kept next to the machine, problems noted on charts kept next to the machine, and following a 5 S exercise, vital components made visible by replacing (where possible) steel covers with transparent plastic or glass. Also, following 5 S, and leaks or drips are more easily seen.

RED TAGS – Red tags are a common form of visible TPM. Maintenance "concerns" are written on red tags and hung on a prominent board on the shop floor. They remain there until action is taken. Red tags usually cover concerns that cannot be dealt with by operators.

VISUAL CHECKLISTS – Monitoring is very important in TPM. Therefore checklists are common. The status of each workcentre should be monitored against written standards, kept at the workplace. Checklists should be developed by the operators doing the work, not by an industrial engineer. They should also incorporate drawings or photos. A Japanese idea is that self developed sheets may not look as good as "professionally" developed sheets, but they are more effective.

USE OF ALL SENSES – Most humans come to work with "hidden extras" which are not always used to best effect. So use them. First, there's the brain. TPM would like operators to think of better ways of maintaining equipment, keeping records, and making improvements. Then, there are the senses of smell, hearing, touch, seeing, and vibration detection. Humans are especially good at detecting changes in these (for example, you may not be aware of a noise, but will notice when the note changes). So tell the team leader, report it, record it. This is a simple, but not to be underestimated, form of condition monitoring.

OWNERSHIP – The principle is, if you are responsible or if it's your own you will look after it better, and uptime will improve. Don't pass the buck. Carry out "aircraft style" checklists at the start of the shift. Learn how to do simple maintenance tasks yourself. Keep inexpensive wearing components and lubrication to hand. Keep your own records.

BOTTLENECKS – The importance of bottlenecks is discussed elsewhere in this publication (in the Goldratt section). But bottlenecks are important for TPM also. First priority should be given to a 6 big losses analysis at bottlenecks, and to maintenance kaizen activities at bottlenecks. Keep especially good maintenance records at bottlenecks.

FAILURE MODES AND SCHEDULED MAINTENANCE – In classic Preventive Maintenance, a "bathtub" curve was often assumed (i.e. high failure rate early on, dropping to a low and continuing failure rate, then increasing at wearout). Routine maintenance is then scheduled just before the risk rate starts to increase. Today, we know that not all equipment has this pattern. Some may not have early high failure, some may not have sudden wearout, some may exhibit a continuous incline, etc. The point is you need to know the failure mode in order to undertake good scheduled maintenance practice. So, data needs to be recorded, the best way being automatically, for instance the number of strokes on a press for each die. And operators (who often have an inherent knowledge of failure modes) should be consulted. A maintenance cycle should be developed much like the cycle-counting concept, which visits important machines more frequently, allocates responsibility, and aims to improve not just maintain.

CONDITION MONITORING – Condition monitoring is a specialist function in TPM, but in some environments (for example heavy and rotating machinery) an important means to reduce cost. Methods include vibration detection, temperature monitoring, bearing monitoring, emission monitoring, and oil analysis. Today, there are hand-held, and computer linked, devices to assist.

INFORMATION SYSTEMS – Information systems were always an important part of PM, and remain so with TPM. However, their scope is extended from machines to include operator, safety and energy issues but also to allow for workplace data recording.

DESIGN AND ADMINISTRATION, AND BENCHMARKING – Today, TPM is beginning to be seen in administrative and white-collar areas. Of course, there are computers, photocopiers, and fax machines but there also tidy (?) desks, filing cabinets, and refreshment rooms. Progressive companies are beginning to cater for TPM in product design. And, benchmarking, as usual, is useful.

FURTHER READING:
Seiichi Nakajima (Ed), *TPM Development Program,* Productivity Press, Cambridge MA, 1989, ISBN 0-915299-37-2
Seiichi Nakajima, *Introduction to TPM,* Productivity Press, Cambridge MA, 1988, ISBN 0-915299-23-2
Peter Willmott, *Total Productive Maintenance: The Western Way,* Butterworth Heinemann, Oxford, 1994, ISBN 0-7506-1925-2
John Moubray, *Reliability Centred Maintenance,* (Second edition), Butterworth Heinemann, Oxford
Nick Rich, a great new book forthcoming!

OVERALL EQUIPMENT EFFECTIVENESS (OEE)

OEE = availability x performance rate x quality rate

where

availability = $\frac{(\text{planned run time} - \text{downtime})}{\text{planned run time}}$ x 100

note: planned run time is the total time when needed

performance = $\frac{(\text{units produced} \times \text{design cycle time})}{\text{actual run time}}$ x 100

or $\frac{(\text{cycle time} \times \text{quantity produced})}{\text{actual run time}}$ x 1000

(note that this element often is capped at a maximum of 100 %)

quality rate = $\frac{(\text{total output} - \text{defects})}{\text{total output}}$ x 100

or (parts right first time) / (completed cycles) x 100

Notice:

→ OEE is a very severe test since it is the product of three factors. If each factor were a high 90%, then the OEE would be only 72%. (Actually, 85% is good performance in world terms).

→ OEE is directly related to the 6 big losses:

Breakdown and Changeover form the availability measure
Minor Stoppages and Reduced Speed form the performance measure
Non conforming items and changeover scrap form the quality measure

The components of OEE should be tracked separately. It is a good idea to display 4 graphs; one for overall OEE, and one each for the 3 elements. Below each graph, the reasons may be given in the form of a fishbone diagram.

Where there are several similar machines, say presses a very useful exercise is to identify the highest performing machine on each of the three dimensions, and then to calculate the current "best demonstrated practice". This would be the current best OEE in the shop if the best feature of each were used. This gives an immediate, attainable target. Find out why or how the best figures are obtained for the best machine in each category.

OEE figures often come as a shock to management. They should certainly be calculated before any capital acquisitions are made, and as an indicator for continual improvement activities.

Some plants try to calculate an overall OEE for the entire plant. This questionable practice involves weighting the various OEE machines on some criteria say by total output. The problem is so much time is spent arguing about the best weightings, you may never get around to actually improving OEE.

ROOT CAUSE PROBLEM SOLVING

The emphasis on "root cause" problem solving is fundamental to the philosophies of JIT, lean manufacturing, continuous improvement, the Toyota production system, and TQM. It means solving problems at the root rather than at the superficial or immediately obvious levels. But how do you get to the root cause? In the following sections two techniques are examined. But first, we should look at the whole concept of root cause analysis.

In a thoughtful article Finlow-Bates concludes that there are no ultimate root causes. Rather, root causes are dependent upon the problem owner; there can be more than one potential root cause and that the final choice of root cause cannot be made until the economics of possible solutions have been considered. He illustrates the point by the example of a delivery failure. The root cause for the customer is that the parcel is late. The root case for the delivery company is that the problem delivery failure was due to the van not starting which can be traced to the root cause of a leaking underground tank. For the tank supplier the root cause was a failure in the solder. For the solder supplier the root cause was …. Each person along the chain is not interested in the problems of lower echelons. Each of these causes represents a failure in control or in communication. The real issue is therefore not what is the root cause, but how can be problem be (temporarily?) solved most economically and effectively to prevent recurrence.

Finlow-Bates suggests following six steps:

→   What is the unwanted effect? (Finlow-Bates suggests two words; subject and deviation, for example parcels late)

→   What is the direct physical cause?

→   Follow the direct physical line of the cause. For example, parcels late, van won't start, etc. This establishes the "staircase"

→   Ask who owns the problem at each stage.

→   Identify where should one intervene in the staircase to effect a long-term solutions.

→   Identify the most cost-effective of the solutions.

The 5 Whys, Goldratt's Theory of Constraints and Thinking Process, and Barrier Analysis. Goldratt's Thinking Process is dealt with in a separate later section, so here we look at the other two.

THE 5 WHYS

The 5 Whys simply requires that the user ask "why?" several times over. The technique is called the "5 Whys" because it is the experience of its inventor, the Toyota company, that "why" needs to be asked successively five times before the root cause is established.

This simple but very effective technique really amounts to a questioning attitude. Never accept the first reason given; always probe behind the answer. It goes along with the philosophy that a defect or problem is something precious; not to be wasted by merely solving it, but taking full benefit by exposing the underlying causes that have led to it in the first place. Many believe that it is this unrelenting seeking out of root causes that have given the Japanese motor industry the edge on quality, reliability and productivity.

An example follows: A door does not appear to close as well as it should. Why? Because the alignment is not perfect. Why? Because the hinges are not always located in exactly the right place. Why? Because, although the robot that locates the hinge has high consistency, the frame onto which it is fixed is not always resting in exactly the same place. Why? Because the overall unit containing the frame is not stiff enough. Why? Because stiffness of the unit during manufacture does not appear to have been fully accounted for. So the real solution is to look at the redesign of the unit for manufacture.

Perhaps there are even more Whys. Why did this happen in the first place? (Insufficient co-operation between design and manufacturing.) Why so? (It was a rushed priority.) Why? (Marketing had not given sufficient notice.) Why? And so on.

The 5 why analysis gives guidance to the role of an effective quality department. With total quality established, much responsibility for quality will be placed "at source", that is with the person that makes it. But this is not sufficient. The quality professionals need to be spending more time on the detective work of tracing problems to their root cause. This is real continuous improvement and prevention.

A variation of the 5 Why technique is the "5 How" technique. This is often used in tracing the cause of a failure in a product or in service delivery. ("How did that happen?"....) The thinking and procedure is exactly the same.

BARRIER ANALYSIS

Barrier Analysis (Wilson et al) may be used where implementation problems are being experienced. It amounts to a straightforward set of questions that are addressed to an unwanted problem or event:

→ What are the threats, hazards or potential problems that can influence the situation? Threats may be physical or psychological, or influence status, security, or self esteem.

→ Who or what are the "Targets" for change? In any change there will be victims and beneficiaries, some perhaps unintended. It is useful to list these. The target may be human, animal, organisation, environment, group, team, family, or other.

→ What are the barriers? These may be physical, geographic, communication, language, culture, administrative, organisational. Also, what are the safeguards that are supposed to be in place to make the change easier or more acceptable, and if they are not in place, why are they not. Should the threat be isolated, or should the target be isolated, or both?

→ What is the "Trace". That is, what is the sequence of events or history that has lead up to this situation? Real or imaginary.

Remember that people don't resist change, they resist being changed.

FURTHER READING:
T Finlow-Bates, "The Root Cause Myth", *The TQM Magazine,* Volume 10 Number 1, 1998, pp10-15
The following book has some useful material in relation to the last section, but also much material of low relevance
Paul Wilson, Larry Dell, Gaylord Anderson, *Root Cause Analysis: A Tool for Total Quality Management,* ASQC Quality Press, Milwaukee, WI, 1993, ISBN 0-97389-163-5

Business Process Reengineering

Since the early 1990s, there has been an explosion of interest on the topic of Business Process Reengineering (BPR), also known as Business Process Redesign. Yet many claim that it is not new but just a redefinition of Systems Analysis (see The Soft Systems Methodology) or Time Based Competition (see Time Charting and Analysis), or "JIT in the Office". These views have some validity. Indeed, BPR incorporates a "systems view", recognises the importance of time, and time-base approaches such as simultaneous engineering, and builds in the JIT /Lean views about waste reduction, simplicity, small frequent batches, and supplier partnerships. BPR can also be seen as a natural extension of Total Quality; it recognises that customers want value and value is made up from quality, time, and cost, and delivery. As for the newness, as noted in the section on business process mapping, Joseph Juran carried out a BPR exercise in 1941.

The essence of BPR sees the organisation as a set of processes that together achieve the core business objectives. This is as distinct from the traditional view of organisation with sees functions as distinct "silos". Customers, of course, are not interested in the way the business is organised; they want the product. The silo view only leads to delay and waste. There are some advantages of silos, however, mainly to do with the fostering of specialist skills. So BPR shifts the emphasis from strong vertical silos but weak cross processes, to strong processes but weaker silos. A lecturer cannot run a good course by herself. She needs admin support, library support, support from maintenance to ensure the equipment is working, and so on. This is process or cross-functional management.

A process is a system of activities that lead to the satisfaction of a customer by producing a particular output. Process is fundamental to Lean. BPR looks at the core processes in the organisation and reorganises and simplifies accordingly. Most organisations will have less than 8 core processes: the essence of what the organisation does. Internal customers form a logical chain focusing on external customers; they do not look upwards to serving the boss, but sideways to serving the customer. The lack of a process view may help explain why so many good organisations, with good people, and good product ideas, fail to perform well. They are hide bound by the organisation. BPR is not matrix organisation, or automation ("don't automate, obliterate!", says Hammer), or more effective information technology, or even as some would have us believe, an improved form of computer systems analysis.

Once the core processes have been identified, and the goal of each defined, one asks the simple yet radical question "what are the minimum necessary activities to achieve this goal?", ignoring existing functional departments. This can, and has, led to massive reorganisation; large staff cuts, but also to dramatic reductions in lead-time and improvements in customer service.

Unlike Kaizen that emphasises continuous incremental improvements, BPR goes for a step-function leap in performance. But unlike Kaikaku which aims at a short term productivity "blitz" in a small area, BPR is far more wide ranging. BPR often starts with a blank sheet of paper, Kaizen with existing processes. BPR is top-down management driven; Kaizen relies upon operator initiatives. So BPR and Kaizen should be recognised as partners.

According to BPR Guru Michael Hammer, BPR has the following characteristics:

➔   Several jobs are combined into one ("is it essential to have a qualified accountant do that?", "does it really have to go to another person?")

➔   Workers make decisions ("why does that decision have to be referred to the boss?"); The steps in the process are performed in a natural order (can process steps be overlapped, is that non-customer benefiting task necessary?)

→ Processes have multiple versions (one simple route for the routine many, another for the complex few, rather than all going the same way)

→ Work is performed where it makes most sense, (on the spot, not referring it back to a specialist if possible)

→ Checks and controls are reduced (inspect and fix defects immediately, cut out the waste of unnecessary checks)

→ Reconciliation is minimised (build supplier partnerships with trust); A case manager provides a single point of contact (customers don't get shunted around), and

→ Hybrid centralised / decentralised operations are prevalent (make use of common information systems, but decentralise decision making authority.) So one can see that teams, and especially self-directed teams, are central to BPR.

The Rummler and Brache Matrix

To implement BPR usually involves a fundamental examination of company systems. To do this Rummler and Brache have suggested a most useful framework. This involves a two dimensional matrix of 9 cells. The columns are Goals, Design, and Management and the rows are Organisation Level, Process Level, and Job or Task Level. The suggestion is that there are three levels to consider, which form a hierarchy. The organisation is made up of processes and each process is made up of jobs and tasks. These must all be defined. Then on each level we need to clarify the goals, to consider the design or structure, and to work out how to managed and measure the organisation, each process and each task within each process. The framework is also an excellent framework for Hoshin planning and management, discussed in the Planning section of this book.

Following Up

Once this framework has been worked through, detailed flowcharts or "process maps" can be drawn. Two maps should be drawn for each process: an "is" map and a "should be" (detailing the ideal state). The mapping of business processes is given attention in a separate section, together with other mapping tools.

There are many techniques associated with the various stages of a BPR project. An indication is given in the figure. This figure uses the overall soft systems methodology as a framework. Notice that once the "real world" analysis has been completed, good BPR involves taking a step back. (What Davenport calls a "vision statement" and Hammer calls "starting with a blank sheet of paper")? If you don't do the conceptual stage, you are really doing work-study or a kaikaku exercise, not BPR.

Many of the techniques are further described in this book. Others are given in the companion volume, *The Quality 60*. Implementation often requires what Hammer refers to as a "Process Tsar" - this has similarities with the strong project manager found in concurrent engineering design activities.

Workflow software is increasingly being used in BPR implementations. An example is Lotus Notes, suitably adapted. Such software enables a job to be electronically routed from workstation to workstation, irrespective of department. Jobs can have multiple versions, be signed off at each stage, be routed to alternative workcentres, and be monitored for progress.

Of course, BPR is not just technique. To be successful a complete change in culture is required, from departmental thinking to process thinking. That is the really hard part!

BUSINESS PROCESS REENGINEERING
Stages and Techniques
Note : The framework follows that of Checkland's
Soft Systems Methodology

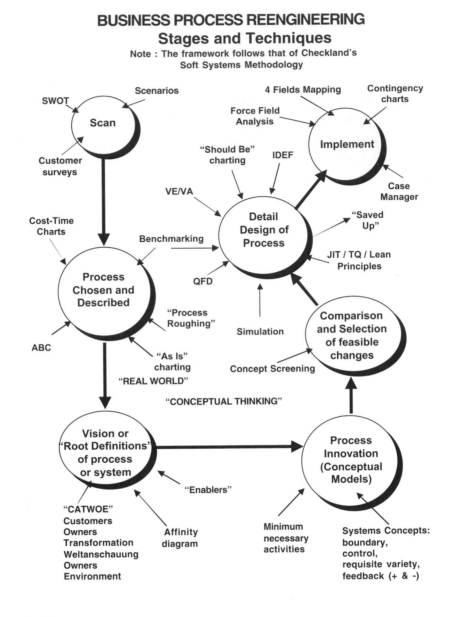

FURTHER READING:

Michael Hammer and James Champy, *Reengineering the Corporation,* Nicholas Brealey Publishing, 1993

Geary Rummler and Alan Brache, *Improving Performance,* Jossey Bass, 1990

Thomas Davenport, Process Innovation, Harvard Business School Press, 1993.

Raymond Manganelli and Mark Klein, *The REengineering Handbook,* AmaCom, New York, 1994, ISBN 0-8144-7923-5

Institute Of Business Process Reengineering
1 Cecil Court, London Road, Enfield, Middlesex, EN2 3AF Tel 0181 366 6718

Workflow
see http://www.aiai.ed.ac.uk/wfmc
Reference
Peter Lawrence (ed) Workflow Handbook, Wiley, 1997

PRODUCTION

- Little's Law
- Kanban
- Batch Sizing
- Changeover Reduction
- Mixed Model Production
- Runners, Repeaters, Strangers
- Demand Smoothing (Heijunka)
- Group Technology and Cellular Manufacturing
- Inventory Issues: Cost, Waste, Safety Stocks
- Visual and Audio Management
- Point of Production Control

LITTLE'S LAW

Little's Law is an often ignored but fundamental relationship in operations, named after John Little who worked in area of queuing theory in the 1960's. It is:

$$WIP = \text{production rate} \quad x \quad \text{lead time}$$
$$\text{or}$$
$$= \text{rate of product arrivals} \quad x \quad \text{lead time}$$

$$\text{or Lead Time} = WIP / \text{production rate}$$

So if the lead-time is increased the WIP (but not necessarily raw materials) will increase. And if the production rate (in parts per day) increases, the lead-time decreases. This may sound obvious, and indeed it is obvious where there is a single product, but beware it is often ignored or violated in multi-product or multi stage situations.

Target lead times should be checked, whether for JIT or MRP, against this formula. George Plossl, production control guru, is famous for saying "lead time is what you say it is". Provided WIP and or the production rate is changed in sympathy, he is correct. If they are not changed, the statement is not correct.

Notice also that by increasing the production rate, WIP will inevitably increase. Hence Ohno's warning that overproduction is the prime sin. The law might also be cited as the basis for Goldratt's Drum Buffer, Rope approach, for Kanban, and variations such as the CONWIP (constant WIP) system.

Little's Law can be applied as a test on a wide scale - say across a full supply chain - or on a much smaller scale - say within a cell. In a supply chain:

→ test for WIP to discover how much WIP is "dead" given the lead time and throughput rate performance, or

→ what the realistic levels of WIP should be given the target lead time and throughput rate, or

→ what lead-time is implied by current levels of WIP and throughput.
Very revealing.

Kanban

Kanban has been around for many years and is well established in a large number of companies. It is the classic signalling device for production pull systems. Nevertheless there remain uncertainties about types and quantities. For a few, kanban is still a new concept. Others may have decided that pull systems are not for them; they should think again in the light of new types of pull system. This article attempts a summary of the old and the new.

Single Card Kanban

Traditional kanban is suitable in all stable manufacturing environments where there is repetitive production. In practice, the single card kanban category is by far the most popular type. It is easy to understand, easy to see, and reasonably easy to install. Single card kanban means that a single card (or pull signal) operates between each pair of workstations. Although there may be several single-card kanbans in a loop between a pair of workstations, each kanban is the authorisation to both make a part or product and to move it. Two major categories are product kanban and generic kanban.

Product Kanban

Product kanban (or "replacement kanban") is the simplest form of pull system. With this type, whenever a product is called for from it is simply replaced. If there is no call, there is no authorisation so there is no production. In practice, the variations of this type include kanban squares (a vacant square is the authorisation to fill the square with another similar part), cards (which are returned to the feeding workstation to authorise it to make a replacement quantity as specified on the card), and other variations such as "faxban" or "e-ban" (which operate in exactly the same way as cards, except that the pull signals are not physical).

Product Kanban with Multiple Products

(a) Sequential Operations

In sequential operations, having several different products, product kanban can be used between stations provided there are not too many products. Here, one partly completed product of each type is placed as buffer between each workstation. If product A is called for at the end of the line, this triggers sequential pull signals to make a replacement A. The other products do not move, until they are called for. This system allows a quick response build from a limited selection of products, but of course has the penalty of holding intermediate buffers of part completed products of each type. Hence this system becomes impractical for more than a handful of products. The generic kanban type should then be used, as explained below.

(b) Assemble to Order Operations

A variation that is employed in several assemble-to-order operations (for instance, personal computer "make to order") involves simply having shelves with at least one or two of all parts and subassemblies available surrounding the final assembly area. When an order comes in, it is simply configured from the appropriate shelves. This therefore creates a blank space on the shelf that is the signal for subassembly areas to replace that subassembly. Subassembly areas are themselves arranged into cells that pull parts from the shelf, and hence back to the store. In this way, literally millions of different configurations can be made under a pull system, provided the final products are designed to accommodate a variety of different but similarly sized modules.

(c) Operations where there is Changeover and/or Changing Priorities.

Where there is changeover, a priority kanban board is the usual option. A priority kanban board displays all the products that go through the workcentre. For each product a number of kanbans are hung on the board (See below for calculation of the number of kanbans). The kanbans themselves are colour coded or alternatively there are bands of green, yellow, and red painted on the board to indicate priority. A kanban hanging in the green zone is a low priority authorisation to make a replacement par. A kanban hanging in the yellow zone indicates higher priority and a kanban hanging in the red zone would normally indicate that that product should be the very next one that should be made. The board therefore indicates at a glance the backlog situation. Kanbans are hung on the board for each product in the order green, yellow, red, but are replenished in the order red, yellow, and green. An operator looking at the board is authorised to make a batch quantity covering the red zone, or if there is more time the red plus the yellow zone, or if there is even more time the red plus the yellow plus the green zone. In slack times, the operator may decide to just replenish the green kanbans. See the figure

Priority Kanban Board

the priority is to make at least one batch of P5

(d) Product Kanban with Synchronised Operations

Where there are several legs in a bill of material or assembly structure, synchronisation can be achieved by variations of so-called "golf ball" kanban. Here, as the main build progresses, signals are sent to areas producing supporting assemblies to warn them to prepare the appropriate assemblies "just in time" to meet up with the main build as it progresses along the line. Different colour "golf balls" are moved (often blown by air or send electronically) to the subassembly stations to signal them to prepare the exact required subassembly. This form of kanban can be used internally (say to prepare different windscreens or coloured bumpers) to go onto particular cars, or externally (for instance when sent to external seat suppliers to prepare the exact sequence of seats to meet up with a particular sequence of cars).

EMERGENCY KANBAN

Emergency kanban is a "special event" kanban that is inserted in kanban loops to compensate for unusual circumstances. Such kanban cards are of a different colour so that they may be distinguished easily. Such kanbans automatically go to the head of the queue so their requirements are dealt with as soon as possible. Having produced the additional quantity, emergency kanbans are withdrawn.

A variation is additional kanbans that are inserted to meet seasonal demand or to compensate for transport disruption, such as rail disruption or poor weather. These cards are also withdrawn as soon as possible.

GENERIC KANBAN

Generic (or "capacity") Kanban authorise feeding workcentres to make a part, but do not specify what part is to be made. The part to be made is specified via a manifest or a "broadcast" system. It is therefore the preferable pull system where there are a large number of products, all of which have similar routings and fairly similar time requirements at each workstation. Generic kanban has less WIP than product kanban, but the response time is slower.

RULES OF KANBAN

Downstream operations make to demand. Never overproduce.
Demands are placed on upstream operations by means of cards or other signals
Authorisation to produce is by card (or signal) only.
Each kanban card circulates between a particular pair of workstations only.
Quality at Source is a requirement. Only good items are sent downstream.
The number of kanbans should be reduced as problems decrease.

DUAL CARD KANBAN

Toyota and a few other manufacturers use "dual card" kanban. This can be a tighter form of pull system. Instead of one all-purpose card, the dual card system has both "production" kanbans (with authorise production) and "conveyance" kanbans (which authorise movement). Production kanbans stay at a particular workcentre and alternate from input board to finished goods container with production kanban attached. Conveyance kanbans stay between a particular pair of workstations and alternate between conveyance card mailbox and full container (with conveyance card attached) moved between workstations.

The great thing about dual card kanban is that it allows lot splitting. The transfer batch quantity between work stations, governed by conveyance kanbans, may be a smaller quantity than the production batch size, governed by production kanbans.

A material handler collects up the conveyance kanbans from the mailbox (at Toyota a tune sounds to warn of this event) and takes them to the appropriate feeder workstation. There, the material handler detaches the production kanban from the full container, and attaches the conveyance kanban to the container. The production kanbans are returned to the kanban board of the workstation. When work starts on the batch, as authorised by the production kanban, the operator detaches the conveyance kanban from the container and hangs it on the mailbox for the upstream conveyance.

NUMBERS OF KANBAN CARDS

GENERAL – In line with Lean Manufacturing, the correct answer to the question of the number of kanban cards should generally be "less than last time!" The well-known water and rocks analogy applies. That is, reduce the inventory levels by removing a kanban (or by reducing the kanban quantity) and "expose the rocks". Note that the philosophy of gradually reducing inventory by removing kanbans is "win-win" approach: either nothing will happen in which case you have "won" because you have found that you can run a little tighter or you "hit a rock" in which case you have also "won" because you have hit not just any old rock, but the most pressing rock or constraint. This is what Toyota has done for decades.

The general rule on kanbans is therefore to start "loose", with a generous amount of safety stock, and to move towards "tight kanban" gradually, but steadily.

Of course, it would be unwise to jump into this policy. There are a number of prerequisites for successful kanban. These include reasonably stable demand, reasonably capable processes, preventative maintenance or TPM to ensure tat breakdown stoppages are not endemic, probably reasonably short changeover times, and a disciplined workforce - including management - to ensure that kanban rules are maintained. Given that all of these are in place, and that the company will move from "loose" to "tight" kanban, it is still necessary to be able to establish the approximate number of kanban cards.

CALCULATING THE NUMBER OF CARDS

In general, kanban works like the traditional two-bin system. In the two-bin system the reorder point ROP is calculated thus

$$ROP = D \times LT + SS$$

where D = demand during the lead-time LT between placing and order and receiving delivery, and SS is the safety stock. This familiar formula is the basis for all kanban calculations.

If the container or stillage quantity is Q, then the number of kanbans is simply

$$N = (D \times LT + SS) / Q$$

where N should be rounded up, and should be at least 2 unless the production system is very responsive.

1. NUMBER OF CARDS FOR ASSEMBLY OPERATIONS OR FROM SUPPLIERS

In repetitive assembly operations where there is no changeover, the demand is expressed in units per day, and the lead time LT in the fraction of the day required to go through all the necessary steps between "placing the order" (hanging the kanban on the board) and receiving it. This would normally include the usual lead time elements of run + wait + move. Note that run time should be the time to fill the container, wait time should include both pre- and post-waiting for movement and waiting on the kanban board or mailbox before the order is actioned. Where parts are obtained from an external supplier, the lead-time would be the expected lead-time for delivery as used in any inventory calculation. Demand and lead-time should always be expressed in compatible units; say demand per week and lead-time in weeks.

Safety stock should also be allowed. This would reflect the any uncertainties in delivery, quality, breakdown or other disruption. Note two points. First, the principle of moving from "loose" to "tight" pull and second, the fact that safety stock has usually already been somewhat allowed for in the rounding up calculation to calculate the number of cards.

2. NUMBER OF KANBANS WHERE THERE IS CHANGEOVER.

Where there are multiple products moving through a workcentre, and where there is changeover involved, the calculations become more complex. However, the basic formula remains valid.

In a Press Shop, for example, multiple products must go through a press. There may be a priority kanban board governing the control of sequencing. Some pressings would be repeaters, perhaps made every day, but others more like "strangers" made regularly but much less frequently. The number of kanbans hanging on the board must be capable of responding to the demands placed on the shop.

The correct or optimal number of changeovers in a sequence or "campaign" of making all products is a dealt with elsewhere (Bicheno and Niesmann, 1999) but here it will be assumed that these relative frequencies and batch sizes have been determined. (It should be noted that most press shops adopt (hopefully!) sensible rules of thumb rather than trying to optimise.)

The requirement is to first determine the lead-time for each product. This will reflect the frequency with which each product is run. The frequency of runs should take into account the demand and the costs of the parts and of course the capacity of the shop. This is given for product y by

$$LT_y = \text{total campaign length} / (\text{number of setups for y})$$

The formula for the number of kanbans for product y is

$$N_y = (D_y \times LT_y + SS_y) / Q_y$$

The container quantity Q_y should be a "nice round number" taking into account practical considerations (such as a preference for human-movable containers), but also the balance of takt time (shift time divided by demand per shift) and changeover time. The ideal batch size is that for which the sum of changeover plus run times for all products exactly matches demand in the same length of time. For example, there are 2 products, changeover time is 30 minutes, run time is 1 minute per product and demand rate is 15 per hour for each product (or a takt time of 4 minutes). Ideal batch size would be 30. (Notice that the EOQ is not used!) Container quantity should be a convenient factor of 30, such as 10, 15, 30, but not more than 30 because this would necessitate waiting for the next changeover.

Example: There are 3 products A, B and C that go through a press. Container quantity is 50 for products A and C and 100 for B. All changeovers take 30 minutes. Total campaign length is 2 days. Normal planned production is A:B:A:C.

	A	B	C
demand / day	300	500	100
setups per campaign	2	1	1
safety stock	100	50	50
and			
LTy	1 day	2 days	2 days
and			
Number of kanbans	8	10.5=11	5

These kanbans would be hung on a board, perhaps with priorities arranged as follows.

Red zone	2	2	1
Yellow zone	4	6	3
Green zone	2	3	1

This is the case for "loose" kanban. For tight kanban the actual campaign length should be calculated. This should include the sum of setup plus run times for all products, and allow for collection of kanban cards and delivery to the point of requirement. This total time should be divided by OEE (overall equipment effectiveness = availability x speed utilisation x quality rate). A check should be made for feasibility, that is whether production during the campaign length so calculated is less than actual average demand during this length of time.

In the preceding sections, traditional kanban has been explained. The weakness of traditional kanban is that it assumes repetitive production (even where generic kanban is used) and also a fairly level schedule. Where the schedule is not level, quite significant buffer inventories between the various stages may be idle for lengthy periods, waiting to be pulled. This is of course "muda". Further complications are routings that may vary significantly between products, and variation in processing times resulting in imbalanced lines and temporary "bottlenecks". In such circumstances traditional kanban systems can sometimes have more inventory than MRP push systems. Some variations have been developed to overcome these limitations.

Notice also that the number of kanbans depends on demand. This means that when demand changes, the number of kanbans should change. In an unstable environment there could be quite a bit of adding and subtracting kanbans. Even where there are occasional changes to plateau levels of smoothed-demand, adjustment is required. This means the schedulers have to be vigilant. Raymond Louis suggests than an MRP system is used to generate the required number of kanbans. This does not sound like generally good advice to the writer. Apart from sounding like a reversion to job cards, the philosophy of MRP is inherently that of the job shop rather than the flow shop. MRP is fine for planning, but not for execution. There may be exceptions, but the following offer more promise.

CONWIP

CONWIP or "constant work in progress" (Hopp and Spearman, 1996) links the last process with the first by means of a job kanban card. Cards do not operate between each pair of workstations as in traditional kanban, but instead cards follow the product or batch through all stages in a section. As a product or batch is completed at the last process, the card is send to the first process thereby authorising the start of a new batch. The CONWIP card loop is a whole assembly line, a cell, or a whole factory. CONWIP cards are not product specific. They authorise the start of production of a batch or product of whatever type is required. In this sense they are like generic or capacity kanbans.

CONWIP automatically results in accumulations of inventory in front of temporary bottlenecks, which is just where it is required. There is a similarity with the OPT type "drum, buffer, rope" which links bottleneck workcentre to gateway workcentre and places a "time buffer" in front of the bottleneck. However, with CONWIP the bottleneck does not have to be identified (indeed it may shift) and the time buffer does not need to be calculated.

The number of cards is calculated directly from WIP which is

WIP = feasible cycle time   x   rate of production

= minutes   x   jobs per minute

The feasible cycle time is the total lead-time through the series of processes covered by the CONWIP loop. Begin with a generous estimate and reduce. The usual minimum value is the sum of setup plus run plus move, except where overlapping of a batch is the norm.

minimum number of cards = WIP / average batch size

Electronic signals, faxban and so on, of course, can replace CONWIP "cards", on. A priority kanban board (or in this case a priority CONWIP board) as described earlier, can also be used at the start of a CONWIP line.

A further extension allows two categories of priority. Normally first in first out (FIFO) is used, but jobs having "hot" CONWIP cards are allowed to jump the queue at the first operation or at buffers set up between CONWIP lines.

Why bother with kanban when there is CONWIP? Because, where production stages are well balanced, it is easier to pick up problems faster with kanban. Kanban is a tighter material control system. However, kanban requires strict operating conditions and higher linearity of flow. Of course it is possible to use both kanban and CONWIP simultaneously; CONWIP to control the main flow and kanban to control parts delivery to the line.

POLCA

CONWIP like kanban requires stable routings. POLCA or "paired cell overlapping loops of cards with authorisation" (Suri, 1998) is a push-pull system which allows different routings and job-shop type operations. The workings of a POLCA system is as follows. Refer to the Figure.

POLCA System

POLCA card A-B must be available to start work at Process A

POLCA card A-B travels from A to B to C and is then returned to A

POLCA cards A-B and B-C must both be available before work can start at B

POLCA cards are made up for each pair of processes that a job must pass through. Here A-B and B-C. Like Kanban cards, POLCA cards are the authorisation to begin work.

→ Planned release of jobs, bearing in mind capacity limitations, is done on an MRPII / finite scheduling system. This determines the time before which jobs may not start, NOT when they are due to start.

→ Each job has a card that travels with it through all workstations. This details all workstations to be visited

➔ Each pair of workstations has a number of POLCA cards assigned to them. The number of cards is calculated by

((ave lead time through 1 + average lead time through 2) x jobs 1-2) / t)
where
jobs 1-2 is the number of jobs planned to visit workcentres 1-2 during t.
t is the planning horizon, for example 20 days

➔ At the first workstation there needs to be a suitable POLCA card available before work can start. ("suitable" means a POLCA card that has the required routing; for example card 1-2 would do, card 1-4 would not)

➔ The POLCA card travels with the job to the next THREE workstations (covering two overlapping loops). After completion at the third workcentre the POLCA card is returned to the first workcentre.

➔ After the work at the first workstation is complete, the job and the POLCA card are moved to the second workstation. At the second workstation work can only start when there is a suitable POLCA card for workstations 2 and 3. So at all workstations except the first, there must be two cards available to authorise production; one from the first loop and one from the second loop. This ensures that no job is started before there is available capacity at the workstation after next.

James Selka of Reliance Gear has pointed out a useful analogy: do not let the aircraft take off before you know that there is space for it to land!

POLCA is a fairly complex system compared with traditional kanban, and should not be used where there is linear repetitive production. Both CONWIP and POLCA can handle non-linear demands and changeover operations. POLCA could be considered where routings are irregular or repeat only at infrequent intervals.

FURTHER READING:

Yashiro Monden, *Toyota Production System*, Second Edition, Chapman & Hall, London, 1994
William Sandras, *Just in Time: Making it Happen,* Oliver Wight, 1989
Wallace Hopp and Mark Spearman, *Factory Physics,* Irwin, Chicago, 1996
Rajan Suri, *Quick Response Manufacturing,* Productivity Press, Portland OR, 1998
Raymond Louis, *Integrating Kanban with MRPII,* Productivity Press, Portland, OR, 1997

BATCH SIZING

Whilst the Lean ideal is one-piece flow, this is simply not possible in environments such as press shops which have changeover times which far exceed the manufacturing cycle time and the takt time. In such situations, "SSED" (single second exchange of dies) would be necessary to achieve one-piece flow! Even Toyota and Nissan produce in batches in such circumstances. Of course, one should still continue to attack changeover times, since any reduction improves the flow and reduces batch sizes. That is a given. This section gives an introduction to batch sizing and scheduling in situations where changeover remains a significant factor.

First, a few words on the economic batch quantity. From a lean perspective, this approach should be totally rejected. Major criticisms include:

→ no account is taken of takt time or flow rate

→ classic "batch and queue" thinking

→ changeover cost has to be given as a cost per changeover, whereas changeover teams are usually a fixed resource

→ inventory-holding costs are often understated

→ capacity is assumed to be infinite, and

→ demand is constant and uniform - a lean ideal, but sometimes not a practical one.

The general OPT batch sizing guideline is to increase batch sizes on capacity constrained machines, whilst reducing batch sizes on non-constrained machines. If changeover teams are available they should be used to carry out more changeovers on non-constrained machines, with corresponding reduction in batch sizes, so that such machines become fully utilised in either changeover or running. The resulting reduction in WIP can be used to justify employing more resources on changeover. As a general guideline, this makes good sense, and is compatible with lean thinking. However, in many situations the policy is too simplistic as will be shown. Examples are the built-in assumptions that more changeovers do not affect tool life, do not overload first-off testing, and do not require much adjustment time.

MINIMUM BATCH QUANTITY WITH CHANGEOVER

The minimum practical batch quantity when there is changeover is sometimes governed by the external changeover time. In other words, unless the batch is greater than this minimum, the machine will be idle waiting for external changeover operations. This is a reminder that it is not just internal changeover operations that govern batch size. Effort may have to be put into minimising external operations also.

BATCH SIZING WITH TAKT TIME AND CHANGEOVER

The basic case is where the batch size is determined in relation to takt time and changeover time. Here the batch size is determined from the "cycle quantity" which in turn gives the batch size. The optimal, or minimum, cycle quantity occurs when the cycle of changeover times + run times exactly balances the rate of demand or takt time. In other words:

changeover time + run time for a cycle quantity = cycle quantity x takt time

or

cycle quantity = Σ (changeover time) / (overall takt time - unit run time)

where

overall takt time = 60 / Σ (total demand per hour)

and batch size of a product = cycle quantity x product proportion

Example: There are 3 products A,B,C. Changeover time is 30 minutes for all products. Run time on the machine is 5 minutes for all products. Demand rate, or takt time) is 1 every 20 minutes for A, and 1 every 40 minutes for B and C (i.e. the mix is 2:1:1)

Demand per hour is 3 A, 1.5 B, and 1.5 C or a total of 6.

Overall takt time = 60 / 6 = 10 minutes

Cycle quantity = (3 x 30) / (10 - 5) = 90 / 5 = 18

Batch size of A is 18 x 0.5 = 9, batch size of B and C = 18 x .25 = 4,5 or 5

This assumes perfect quality and zero down time. If these do not apply, then

$$\text{cycle quantity} = \frac{(\Sigma \text{ (changeover time) + downtime and rework time)}}{\text{(overall takt time - unit run time)}}$$

Note also that this assumes batch production is 2A, B, C and not A,B,A,C. The latter is of course more in line with lean manufacturing mixed model production. So if mixed model is desired there will have to be one more changeover per cycle. Overall takt time remains the same, but

cycle quantity = (4 * 30) / (10 - 5) = 120 / 5 = 25

and each batch size becomes 25 * .25 = 6.25

or (say) 7A, changeover, 7B, changeover, 7A, changeover, 7C, changeover

Overproduction could be controlled by kanban.

BATCH SIZING WITH CONSTRAINED CAPACITY, CHANGEOVER, AND PARETO DEMAND

A situation found in literally thousands of companies is where a variety of products of differing quantities have to be scheduled through an operation where there remains fairly substantial changeover times. Almost invariably capacity is an issue. Also invariably the product quantities are not uniform- there is a mix of "repeaters" and "strangers" often forming a strong Pareto distribution of demand. This situation is found in press shops, in textile converters, in chemical plants, and in injection operations, to name but a few. Even though a kanban system may be in operation, there are still questions on pull batch quantities, for purchasing, and for sequencing.

Of course, as always one should attack changeover times and work to improve OEE. Also there should be the ongoing consideration as to product contribution and product line rationalisation. This is assumed. The issue remains how to determine batch quantities. This section gives an introduction to the remaining batch-sizing issues assuming that there is one constrained machine through which a whole portfolio of products must be routed. If there is more than one machine, begin by allocating products to machines.

Batch Sizing Toyota Style

The Toyota approach is to assume a seemingly arbitrary split of 90/10 between run time and setup time. However, this approach is based on long experience. Notice that no time is allocated for idle time during a shift. This gives the total available run time, say per week. Based on the average changeover time, it also gives the total number of changeovers during the week. The changeovers are allocated between the part numbers due to be processed on the machine. Are there enough changeovers to run every part number at least once? If no, some parts must be dropped or changeover time reduced. If yes, is there sufficient run time to run all allocated parts? If no, allocate parts to another machine. If yes, is there time left over? If no, run each part number once per week. If yes, have another changeover and halve the batch quantity on that part. Continue until time runs out.

This method has the great virtue of keeping the pressure on changeover times. If changeover times slip, it will not be possible to complete the week's work. So, this method must be accompanied by changeover time monitoring.

Why 90/10? Consider a series of products moving through two stages, say a blanking line and a press line. Changeovers are involved. As batch sizes come down, total lead-time comes down because the split batches can be moved to the next stage sooner. However, there is a limit to this. Eventually changeover times come to dominate, and lead time increases. The point is that queuing and simulation studies show that for a utilisation factor of around 85%, lead-time is minimised at around a 90/10 ratio. A utilisation (or OEE) is achievable at better companies. At utilisation factors of 50%, however, a 97/3 ratio may be better. Is this why Toyota uses 90/10? We don't know.

Another Method

The concept here is to find the batch sizes that will allow the greatest amount of flow together with the lowest overall inventory levels. Consider this: A company makes 3 products A, B and C which go through one machine on which changeover has been reduced to 30 minutes. Demand is in the ratio 4:1:1. The company has made fair progress towards lean and currently produces according to a "mixed model" schedule of 40 A, 10 B, 10 C, 40 A, 10 B, 10 C. Can flow be improved, and inventory cut without a further reduction in changeover? Yes! By moving to 20 A, 10 B, 30 A, 20 C, 30 A, 10 B. This approach involves cutting the batch size of the high demand products whilst simultaneously increasing batch sizes of low demand products.

First, begin by arranging products in Pareto fashion from high demand to low demand.

Second, determine against demonstrated changeover and run times and OEE, the feasible length of time required to run a complete cycle of demand of each product. This requires one setup for each product on the machine, and a batch quantity equal to the demand during the period. The formula is

$$\Sigma \text{ (changeover times) } + \Sigma \text{ (run time x demand during cycle)}$$

The problem is to determine the appropriate feasible cycle. Do this by iteration. Begin with say a day's demand of each product. With one setup per product, is it possible to run this every day? If not, try 2 days, then 3, and so on until a feasible solution is found.

Third, divide this feasible cycle time by the current OEE for the machine, and add any extra time for any other types of stoppage.

Fourth, examine this minimum cycle time against the realities of the plant and decide by how much the minimum cycle time should be rounded up to make a convenient manufacturing cycle. For instance, say the feasible cycle time works out at 6 days or 96 hours. OEE is 70%. Team meetings and TPM activities take 4 hours per week.

Then 96 / 0.7 + 8 (for two weeks) = 145 hours.

The plant currently works 180 hours per week, which is the nearest convenient manufacturing cycle. This means that the plant could run at least one batch of every product every two weeks, with (in this case) 180 - 145 = 35 hours to spare

Now commence the "trade off" process. In general, any product having a demand (or changeover time) greater than 4 times another product should be "traded" by halving the batch quantity of the higher demand product and doubling the batch quantity is the lower demand product, thereby retaining (or approximately retaining) the total overall changeover time. The extra or spare capacity can be used for cases where changeover times differ and for marginal cases.

Finally, having determined the batch sizes, the final requirement is to arrange the products in a mixed model sequence. Beginning with the high demand products and spacing them as evenly as possible does this. Low demand products fill in the gaps.

"Blanking and Press" Batch Sizing, with Changeover

Several companies have the situation where one process involving changeover feeds the next process also involving changeover, but where the numbers of machines in each bank is not the same. The first machine has a much higher rate of throughput than the second does. This is typically the case where blanking presses feed press lines. Often, the blanker is not as capacity constrained as the main presses. This can be a complex scheduling problem, but is a classic case where MRP scheduling gives an extremely poor solution, and where a TOC solution, not carefully applied, will also mislead.

Consider the case where one blanker of rate 200 per hour, making six products, feeds 3 presses of rate 50 per hour each making two products. All changeovers take 1 hour on both blanker and presses.

The problem is to determine the batch sizes that balance the flow. For this simple case this is given by:

Blanker   Press

((batch size / 200) + setup) * no of products = ((batch size / 50) + setup)* no of prod

((batch size/ 200) + 1) * 6 = ((batch size / 50) + 1) * 2

or batch size = 400

So here a larger batch has to be produced on the feeding machine. There will have to be buffer stock held between the processes, but it is possible to flow a small quantity non-stop from blanker to press.

Reference:
Jens Niesmann, *Constrained Batch Sizing in a Lean Environment,* MSc Thesis, University of Buckingham, 1999

CHANGEOVER REDUCTION

Changeover reduction is another pillar of lean manufacturing. The difference between setup and changeover time is that the latter is the time from the last piece of the previous batch to the first good piece in the next batch. It is this that should be minimised. The late Shigeo Shingo has produced the classic work on "SMED", and very little has been added to what he said. Here are a few points:

The classic Shingo methodology is to separate "internal" activities from "external" activities. External or preparation activities should be maximised. Then try to convert some internal activities to external (for example by pre-heating a mould). Then use engineering on the remaining internal activities. There are many tricks, from quick release nuts, to constant platform shims, to multiple hole connections all in one. A marvellous source of ideas is Shingo's book.

→ Measure and record changeover times. Many changeover times have fallen by doing this alone.

→ Put the pressure on reducing and keeping to setup times. See the comments on the 90/10 policy in the Batch Sizing section.

→ Involve the team in analysis. Do not rely only on Industrial Engineers.

→ Make a video, and get operators to record and critique. The video must remain their property. Put their ideas up on a board at the workplace, and prioritise the improvement activities.

→ Consider a financial incentive for quick setup, whilst discouraging incentives for more production.

→ Remember the equation: Changeover time x no of batches = constant. In other words as changeover time comes down, this must be converted into smaller batches. Resist the temptation just to gain extra capacity.

→ Q:How do you get to Carnegie Hall? A:"Practice, man, practice". It's what grand prix teams do.

→ Use trolleys onto which all tools and equipment is placed, and which can be wheeled to the changeover machine

→ Regularity in the schedule helps. If everyone knows that Machine A is changed over every day at 9 a.m., then everyone from forklift driver to setter will be on hand.

→ Tool and die maintenance is a vital, but sometimes overlooked, part of setup reduction. Don't compromise.

→ At bottlenecks, use a team for the changeover, bringing in operators from non-bottleneck machines.

→ Use appropriate quality control procedures to verify good production. See short run SPC and Precontrol charts.

→ Be aware of the optimal sequence of changeover times.

FURTHER READING:
Yasuhiro Monden, *Toyota Production System,* (Second edition), Chapman and Hall, London, 1994
Shigeo Shingo, *SMED,* Productivity Press, Portland, OR.

MIXED MODEL PRODUCTION

Mixed model production aims at minimising the maximum time between any two similar units of production. Thus, instead of AAAABBBB, use ABABABAB. In other words - one piece flow. Why ? To encourage flow. If all A's are made in the morning and all B's in the afternoon, the rate of production and the flow of inventory around the plant will be different between morning and afternoon. There are other reasons too. A cell can be better balanced with mixed model. And the big one: customer service improves as well as inventory levels dropping. The shorter the repetitive cycle, the shorter the necessary forecast horizon, and thus the greater the possibility of making to the customer's true rate of demand. All this is part of Heijunka.

For complex, large variety situations such as car assembly, there are algorithms available to work out the optimal sequence. But for most plants, this is not necessary - you just try to repeat the sequence as often as possible. Teams can get into doing this quite well for themselves. They should work out the best mixed-model sequence for themselves whenever the mix changes, perhaps even once per week. And then work out the cell balance arrangements; the cell should be balanced over the full repeating sequence, the aim is definitely not to equalise every time slot for every product.

Even if you cannot make every major product every day, the aim should be to make major products as often as possible. See the section on runners, repeaters and strangers.

FURTHER READING:

Yasuhiro Monden, *Toyota Production System,* (Second edition), Chapman and Hall, London, 1994, ISBN 0-412-58220-1

RUNNERS, REPEATERS AND STRANGERS

Runners, Repeaters and Strangers is a useful idea for lean scheduling, thought to have originated in Lucas Industries during the late 1980s.

A "runner" is a product or product family having sufficient volume to justify dedicated facilities or manufacturing cells. This does not mean that such facilities need to be utilised all the time, merely that it is economic or strategically justifiable to operate such facilities on an as-and-when basis, and not to share them with other products.

A "repeater" is a product or product family with intermediate volume, where dedicated facilities are not justifiable. Repeaters should be scheduled at regular slots. Even though the quantity may vary, the slot time should remain approximately constant. This brings advantages of order and discipline. For instance, maintenance and tooling know that a particular job requiring a particular die is needed each Tuesday morning, Suppliers get used to the regular order, setup resources are made ready, the forklift truck may be standing by, and so on. Regularity is the key : try for once per day at the same time; if this is not possible then (say) Monday, Wednesday, Friday at the same times; if this is not possible then (say) every week at the same time, and so on.

A "stranger" is a product or family with a low or intermittent volume. Strangers should be fitted into the schedule around the regular repeater slots. They have lowest priority.

So in constructing the production plan or schedule, begin by doing a Pareto analysis to split the products into runner, repeater, stranger categories. Then runners are of little concern so long as there is adequate capacity. They enjoy their own resources. Repeaters form the backbone of the schedule and should be slotted in at regular intervals as often as capacity will allow, maximising flow and minimising inventories. Make transfer batches smaller than production batches. Then fit the strangers around the repeaters.

This is much like the way we run our lives. We have runners, for example heartbeat that goes on all the time, and we don't plan for these. But you may be conscious of keeping your heart in good condition through exercise. Then repeaters: we sleep every night perhaps not for the same length of time but every night. You know, without being told, not to telephone your friends at 3 a.m. Likewise you have breakfast every day. You use the opportunity to talk to the family, because they are all there without having to arrange a special meeting. What you don't do, even though it may appear more efficient, is to have one big breakfast lasting three whole days at the beginning of the month (one "setup"). You organise your food inventories around these regular habits. Then strangers: you do different things each day, but these different activities are slotted in around the regular activities.

Quality Guru, Phil Crosby talks about running you business "like ballet, not hockey". In ballet you rehearse, adjust and do it the same for each performance. In hockey, each game is different. Runners, repeaters, and strangers allow ballet style management. Too often, it is hockey style-- we collapse exhausted in our chair at the end of the week, feeling satisfied but having solved the same old problem for the 500th time.

DEMAND SMOOTHING

Demand smoothing, or Heijunka, is one of pillars of lean manufacture. It is about uniform production scheduling. This involves three related factors: demand smoothing, load levelling, and line balancing. Load levelling involves distributing the available work evenly across the available time periods and is dealt with in the sections on mixed model production, and "runners, repeaters and strangers". Line balancing is discussed in the section on cell manufacture. Here, we concentrate on demand management and parts supply.

Generally, the smoother the demand, the better the flow. What is attempted here is just a few pointers :

→ Make sure that your company does not make demand smoothing harder for itself by policies such as quantity discounts (rather give discounts for regular orders), or monthly sales incentives (rather give incentives for obtaining regular orders).

→ Use the runners, repeaters and strangers concept (see separate section). There is much underlying stability even in apparently disaggregated situations. For example, perhaps the demands for various products are erratic, but do these products share subassemblies, the demand for which may be much more regular ? Try to make each product every day.

→ Use the "variety as late as possible" concept. Do not add variety until the last possible moment. Design has an important role to play here.

→ Use the "available to promise" logic found in most Master Scheduling packages

→ Stabilise manufacturing operations by buffering keeping finished goods stock, whilst replenishing this stock on a pull basis, buffered if necessary.

→ Reduce changeover times so as to make customer pull more possible. Much underlying demand is fairly stable, but becomes unstable when supply chain members distrust response times and inventory availability.

→ Use control limits, much like an SPC chart. As long as demand stays within these limits, don't change the plan. Or, use a CUSUM chart to detect changes to underlying demand. A CUSUM is one of the most effective ways of detecting shifts in demand patterns. (See *The Quality 60* for a section on Cusums).

→ Give priority to regular orders. Don't let bad drive out good. Filter the erratic orders out, and make them in their own slot with lower frequency.

→ Use "under capacity scheduling" to make sure that you hit the production target. This means not scheduling to full capacity, but allowing a buffer period to catch up on problems. If there aren't any problems, do continuous improvement.

→ Stabilise production at the right level in the bill of materials. Perhaps stabilise at the MPS level, and call off via the final assembly schedule.

→ Measure demand variation, report it, discuss it, make people responsible for it - especially Sales and Marketing. Know the tradeoffs between promotions and "everyday low prices" (as Proctor and Gamble were surprised to discover).

→ Work according to medium term forecasts rather than short term call offs. The medium term will be more stable and probably more reliable. Test the reliability of different forecast horizons, and don't be afraid to ignore short-term forecasts.

→ Gear the incentives of distributors to work towards smooth demand.

→ Practice queue control conscientiously. Use the Drum, Buffer, Rope concept (see separate section).

→ Communicate along the supply chain. Try to make at the ultimate customer's takt time. Try to persuade supply chain partners to share information, and be willing to share it yourself.

→ Overproduction is the greatest enemy. Do not fall into the trap of just making a few more while things seem to be going well. This causes disruption in all later stages.

→ Most of all, have a vision of regular, smoothed demand. Identify the barriers that are preventing this from happening, and make appropriate plans

With regard to parts supply, heijunka requires a shift from the traditional approach. Delivery vehicles have to be organised so that they arrive evenly and are unloaded evenly over the course of a day. Window deliveries are required. "Milk rounds" enable vehicles to pick up small quantities from several suppliers more frequently, rather than one large dedicated batch from a supplier with lower frequency. This should mean that the total number of loads or vehicles remains approximately unchanged, but travelling distances may increase slightly. Also, this should mean that in the long run total costs come down, because total inventories are down and production is flowing in a uniform way across the supply chain. The same comments apply for collection of finished parts. Suppliers and transport companies should be measured on their ability not just to deliver good quality on time, but to deliver the exact quantity in the exact delivery window. Try to have a measure which rewards the regularity of flow - this means both manufacturer and supplier need to co-operate. If you do not have such measures you are not going to get truly lean.

FURTHER READING:

Yasuhiro Monden, *Toyota Production System,* (Second edition), Chapman and Hall, London, 1994, ISBN 0-412-58220-1

John Bicheno, *Cause and Effect JIT : The Essentials of Lean Manufacturing,* PICSIE Books, Buckingham, 1994, ISBN 0-9513829-5-0

GROUP TECHNOLOGY AND CELLULAR MANUFACTURING

Group Technology (G.T.) is the production of a part family, of products or services, in one area, comprising all the necessary machines and processes, thereby enabling one-piece flow and drastic reductions in lead time and inventory.

But, GT or cellular manufacturing goes beyond this :

→ It is at heart of JIT, allowing all the things that JIT aims at : flexibility, one-piece flow, responsiveness, visibility, simplicity of control, high quality, minimal inventories, and focus.

→ It is often central to the concept of self directed team working, since all team members, from a variety of skill areas, work together on one clearly-defined product family, in one physical area, with clear responsibility.

→ GT can also mean a classification and coding system to enable the identification of product families, the simplification of designs, and avoidance of "reinventing the wheel".

→ Decentralised scheduling is made possible. The cell is treated as one large work centre. Often, the detailed scheduling is left to the team who can also be responsible for quality, maintenance, leave, and even inventory. This is directly compatible with the self directed work team concept.

→ In white-collar areas, GT or cells is strongly linked with process reengineering (BPR), which has much the same objectives as mentioned above. The business process approach emphasises working by horizontal process instead of in vertical silos which, when this is applied to a focused, multidisciplinary group working in one physical area, is what GT is all about.

→ The concept is also found in simultaneous engineering / concurrent engineering.

Most of these topics are dealt with in separate sections in this book, but it is group technology or cellular manufacturing which is the basic building block.

The results of introducing cells are often dramatic : lead times previously measured in days drops to minutes, with consequent reductions in inventory. Quality often improves with improved visibility, decentralised responsibility, and immediacy of problem solving.

Britain was a world leader in GT in the 1960s with pioneers such as Burbidge and Edwards. Some of the earliest manufacturing examples were found in Britain, although the concept has its origins with Mitrofanov in the Soviet Union during the Second World War. But, generally, group technology only took off in the 1980s when the Japanese brought some of the essential ingredients into the mix : these are flexible labour, emphasis on quality and continuous improvement, attention to maintenance (or TPM) and housekeeping, and perhaps the JIT concept of the level schedule (termed "heijunka" at Toyota).

SETTING UP A CELL

Essentially GT or cellular manufacturing aims at the advantages of mass production and the assembly line (efficiency, one piece flow) without its disadvantages of inflexibility and demotivated workers. So a GT cell is a hybrid between the assembly line and the job shop. To set up a GT cell:

→ Identify part families. These are parts that have similar manufacturing routings. The routings do not have to be exactly the same, and the products may not even look alike. There are some sophisticated methods to identify families (see below), but the "eyeball approach" is often adequate.

➔ Since one cell will be responsible for one product family, volumes must be sufficient for this to be feasible. This may mean, on the one hand, trimming the product range or selecting out only the highest volume products, or on the other hand, changing some existing product routings to enable them to be made within the cell. This therefore may involve engineering and design. Develop the anticipated flow rate by consulting Marketing and Sales. Aim for a capacity that matches demand every week rather than every month. This may involve reducing changeover times, or permanently set up machines

➔ Note that not all processes need to be incorporated within the cell, at least initially. Some process steps may involve outside subcontractors or visits to specialised process centres, such as painting. Such steps may not involve all products in the family. But, it is important to have the aim of what is termed in JIT production "the small machine principle". That is, in selecting future machines always (?) choose the smallest machine. Try to select machines that work at the anticipated flow rate : there is no point in selecting machines that work at several times faster than the flow rate, because overproduction, inventory or other waste is the inevitable result. Also, it may be possible to use old, previously discarded, machines as long as they can hold the required quality. Be cautious therefore in scrapping old machines.

➔ Separate machine jobs / time from operator tasks / time. An operator can tend several machines. See later.

➔ Now collect up all necessary machines to make the product family. Assemble them in the same area in the required sequence, as close as possible to one another. Often a U shaped layout is the aim for visibility and labour flexibility. The aim is to minimise material handling; moving products one at a time, sometimes by hand or by gravity, rather than in containers by forklift.

➔ Select the appropriate tooling for the cell. Ideally the cell should own all tools used by a cell. Some adjustment to routings may be required.

➔ Select the cell team and balance the work. Cross-train the operators. When the cell is busy, move more operators into the cell. When the cell is less busy, fewer operators should tend several machines. This is known as "shojinka" at Toyota. Often, the detail work balancing can be left to the team rather than external industrial engineers. Some cell teams incorporate dedicated maintenance, quality, scheduling, purchasing, and inventory control staff. Here the cell becomes more of a factory within a factory. Decentralised MRP may follow (that is, if MRP is considered necessary at all!)

➔ Reduce the space and flow distance in the cell by :
  - placing machines as close together as possible, even perhaps touching
  - consider vertical placement of machines where possible
  - selecting narrow machines, where possible
  - arranging for machines to have wheels or castors, where possible

➔ - combining operations and controls (for example, several drilling operations done simultaneously, controlled by a single switch)

Operators, Work Rate, and Balancing ("Shojinkja")

Changing the number of operators alters the rate of work through a cell. At Toyota, the starting point is the takt time, that is the unit time required to make a part that will translate into the required daily production. (If 400 parts are required in 400 minutes of operating shift time, the takt time is 1 minute.). Then, the individual work elements are combined so that each operator has a work cycle of less than the takt time. If demand drops the takt time will increase, so fewer operators should be required. For each number of operators, a specific work route is worked out for each operator. At Toyota the cell throughput, maximum takt time, and individual operator routes are displayed on a board at the cell. (This board is known as the NUMMI board at GM, named after the GM/Toyota joint venture in California). Also displayed, usually using magnetic strips, are the individual work elements, scaled to represent time, which can be rearranged jigsaw-style to fit in with any takt time. Operators are encouraged to participate in improvements and timing that will minimise the amount of wasted time. If (say) 3.2 operators are necessary to meet a particular takt time, then 0.8 of an operator's time will be wasted every takt cycle, so the object would be to improve to enable only 3 operators to do the work. An all out attempt will be made to eliminate the 0.2 of operator time every cycle. To enable all operators to work at the same constant rate within a takt time, standard times including rest and delay are not used. Instead, the whole team in a cell take breaks more frequently, but all together.

Refer to the Figure.

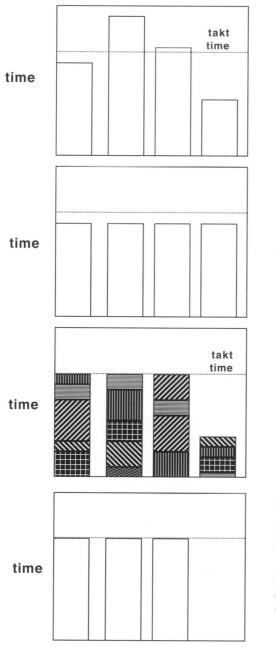

Original work allocation between 4 operators in a cell or on an assembly line.

Takt time is shown

$$\text{Takt time} = \frac{\text{net available time}}{\text{scheduled units}}$$

Here, target will not be met.

Traditional work allocation aims at equalising work cycle.
No notice is taken of takt time. In this case, the work cycle is shorter than takt time so either overproduction or slack time results.

JIT / Lean line balance is done by operators themselves.
Magnetic strips representing detailed work elements are placed on the board, and work allocation adjusted to equal takt time.
Here, the 4th operator has a large block of spare time cycle which may be used for cleanup, work relief of others, etc

Finally, the JIT / Lean cell balance aims to attack the spare time, so as to save an operator who can be used elsewhere (NOT dismissed!)

Line rebalance takes place whenever a change in the takt time occurs - perhaps weekly.

PRODUCTION FLOW ANALYSIS

The late John Burbidge, one of the pioneers of GT, claims that every factory can be converted 100% into a series of cells. His production flow analysis (PFA) technique aims to achieve this. Others claim that a "residual cell" or job shop must inevitably remain of products that cannot be fitted into cells. If this is so, aim to phase such products out or to increase their volumes so as to make cells economic.

What follows is a brief description of a particular form of analysis enabling a job shop to be converted into cells. However, many times, this will not be necessary. What is to be placed in a cell is often obvious. For instance, light pressings, a blister packaging line, assembly, a cell for the approval of building plans by a local authority, or simply a production line which can be dedicated to a particular product family, such as notice boards or tables.

The PFA approach comprises four stages, Factory Flow Analysis, Group Analysis, Line Analysis and Tooling Analysis. All require the component routings. The goal of Factory Flow Analysis aims at identifying the major groups that contain all the machines necessary to complete the major product families. The aim is unidirectional flow and begins by mapping the routings between all departments (all the flows between forging and welding, for example, are counted and the number shown on an arrow joining these departments). This is usually a shock! See the figure. Now examine the flows, Pareto style. The major flows are generally accepted, but minor flows and especially back flows, and two-way flows, need questioning. Can major departments be combined (for instance, most parts made by one department go onto another) ? Burbidge suggests five ways to simplify : rerouting of parts, reallocation of some machines between departments, change of method, change of design, and purchasing instead of making. This should lead a vastly simplified overall flow chart.

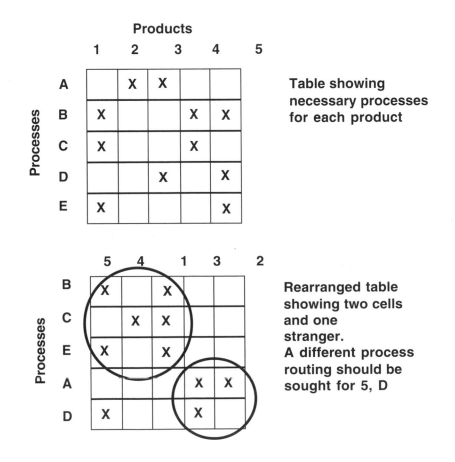

Table showing necessary processes for each product

Rearranged table showing two cells and one stranger.
A different process routing should be sought for 5, D

The Group Analysis stage aims to divide all parts assigned to major groups into smaller product families. In flow analysis the sequence of departments visited is identified. Then we identify which actual machines are visited. A matrix is drawn up with components along the one axis and machines along the other. By manual or computer methods the chart is reordered so as to form product families. See the figure. Thereafter the typical load placed on each cell is compared with the cell capacity.

Line Analysis is concerned with the sequence in which machines are actually laid out. Often, if previous work has been done well this stage is simple, otherwise a repeat of the factory flow analysis stage but this time within a group, is called for. Finally, Tooling Analysis aims at identifying the appropriate tools. Some tool sharing between groups may be required.

Part Classification and Coding is also considered part of GT. Here a classification system is adopted (examples are Brisch and MICLASS but home-grown systems are also possible). The aim is to avoid duplication of design effort and to make sure that each new design conforms to manufacturing requirements and cell compatibility. Today, GT is invariably computerised. Before a designer begins a new design, he or she searches the GT database for components having similar characteristics. The CAD system may constrain designers from selecting inappropriate materials or manufacturing technologies, and GT is also an aid to manufacturing engineers in deciding on appropriate routings and toolings.

FURTHER READING:

John L Burbidge, *The Introduction of Group Technology,* Heinemann, London, 1975

C.C. Gallagher and W.A. Knight, *Group Technology Production Methods in Manufacture,* Ellis Horwood, Chichester, 1986

David Buchanan, "Cellular Manufacturing and the Role of Teams", in John Storey (Ed), *New Wave Manufacturing Strategies,* Chap 10, Paul Chapman, London, 1994

Kirton, Jim and Ellen Brooks, *Cells in Industry : Managing Teams for Profit,* McGraw Hill, Maidenhead, 1994

Michael Maccoby, "Is there a Best Way to Build a Car?", *Harvard Business Review,* Nov-Dec 1997, pp161-171

INVENTORY ISSUES

INVENTORY COST

The topic of inventory cost and value is important in lean operations because both involve deviation from traditional thinking.

The traditional view of inventory carrying cost is that it includes capital cost (the cost of capital or the opportunity cost of capital) and holding cost (costs of the store or warehouse, including space occupied, wages, damage, obsolescence, and material handling equipment in the store). Some of these costs are regarded as fixed or overhead by some companies, but nevertheless are directly attributable to inventory and should be included. So, typical figures would be a capital cost of 10% p.a. and a holding cost of 15% p.a. leading to an inventory carrying cost of 25% p.a.

However, the "lean" view goes beyond this. In most plants inventory actually involves far more cost : inventory takes up space on the factory floor (which not only costs space but also prevents compact layouts which in turn means more material handling and decreased effectiveness of communication), may involve activities such as cycle counting and record keeping, the costs of backflushing activities and other reporting to the MRP system, may also involve defect detection costs which tend to rise with larger batches (if each batch is inspected and an error detected the whole batch must be reworked, if a smaller batch the rework quantity falls). All this is waste, or muda. And, very significantly, large batches of inventory work against regular flow (the ideal of making some of each part every day), which in turn can have an impact on finished goods stocks and on customer service. Small batches, by contrast, enable production at the customer's rate of demand thereby simultaneously decreasing finished goods holdings and improving customer service. So, what is the real carrying cost of inventory ? All we really know is that it is much higher than the carrying cost. How about 50% p.a. ?

If you still believe in the Economic Order Quantity (EOQ) formula, it is

Square Root of (2 x annual demand x order or changeover cost / (unit cost x % carrying cost)).

So, the result of increasing the carrying cost means that the EOQ must decrease. And, if you also work on reducing the costs or ordering or changeover, the EOQ should decrease even further.

INVENTORY WASTE

So what is the lean view of manufacturing inventory ? If you were thinking of running a very lean plant, what inventory is waste or overproduction, and what is the minimum quantity that you should be aiming at ? Again some redefinition from traditional views is necessary.

The traditional view is that buffer stock is necessary to decouple unbalanced operations. The lean view is that buffers are only strictly necessary in front of constrained operations and in front of final assemblies leading from non-bottleneck operations. All other buffers are waste.

The traditional view is that cycle stock is necessary to allow for batch manufacture where there are long changeover times. So cycle stocks build up and diminish in a cycle after operations with changeovers. But the lean view is to "keep it moving" with no changeover delay. Thus cycle stocks are waste, but a form of waste that you may have to put up with for some time.

The traditional view is that work in process inventory is necessary during manufacture. So it is, but how much? The answer is that the ideal is one piece per machine. All other WIP is waste. Remember the comments on buffers above.

The traditional view is that safety stocks are necessary to account for fluctuations in final customer demand, and in supply. The lean view is that some safety stock may be necessary, where demand is absolutely noncontrollable, but one should work towards producing at the same rate as customer demand. And, one should work with suppliers to ensure perfect JIT delivery to the point of use. So for many companies, most of their "safety" stock would be waste.

Finally, the traditional view is that hedging stock is sometimes necessary to avoid price increases or other special non-regular uncertainties. So hedging stock is not waste, provided that it is true one-off type hedging stock. Any regular "hedging" stock is not only waste but is also not hedging stock.

By starting with total inventories, one should be able to categorise into these elements, derive the appropriate quantities, and by subtracting the quantities from the total, arrive at short, medium and ideal inventory targets.

SAFETY STOCKS

Traditionally, safety stock is held as a buffer against uncertainty. A constant quantity is aimed at and, in MRP and reorder point systems, replenished when the level dips below the reorder level. From a lean perspective, this is waste because it does recognise risk. When inventory levels are high, as occurs in batch production immediately following the run, there is minimal risk of stockout. There is only risk during the short period when inventory is low. On the other hand when frequent small batches are being made, there is greater exposure to the risk of stockout. Perhaps therefore more safety stock should be held in this latter case. But not all stockouts will result in lost sales; in some cases customers expect to wait. In other cases a stockout can be catastrophic, resulting in the loss of a customer and future transactions concerning many other products.

Derek Roux of Execulink has developed the "lost sales multiplier" which quantifies this risk of loss. This approach has to be the way to go.

VISUAL AND AUDIO MANAGEMENT

A well-established theme in Lean Operations is visual management or "control by visibility". Visibility has been joined by audio. Visibility fits in well with several other Lean Themes:

→ Speed (no waste of time having to look for information), Improvement (progress should be for all to see, and celebrated).

→ Up to date and clear schedules (via kanban, progress boards, automatic recording).

→ Making problems apparent (via overhead Andon boards or lights).

→ Involvement (clarity on who is doing what and who can do what).

→ Teamworking (making visible the good work of teams).

→ Standardisation (keeping standards up to date by locating them at the workplace).

→ Responsiveness (requiring quick response to maintenance and quality problems via for example a line stop chord or a red tag maintenance board).

Ford Motor Company makes a distinction between visual display, concerned with provision of information, and visual control, concerned with action.

The idea is to be able to gain the maximum amount of operating information and control without having to go off the shop floor - a variation of Gemba management. This applies to operators, supervisors, and managers. A useful quick test of plant capability is simply to note the amount of information on display and how it is kept up to date. In the section that follows, just a few examples of visual management are given

→ Machines: Transparent plastic guards and covers used wherever practical to enable operators and maintenance people to see the innards of machines.

→ OEE charts placed next to machines or at team meeting areas; there should be four graphs - one for overall OEE and one each for the three elements of OEE. Below each graph should be kept a fishbone or CEDAC diagram with the contributing factors.

→ Changeover times should certainly be graphed routinely, to prevent slippage.

→ Lights to indicate status, with the overhead Andon Board linked to computer to record stoppages for later analysis (not blame!)

→ Management: Is it possible to have the production control and scheduling office on the shop floor?

→ Cost, Quality, Delivery performance should be a central trio on display, possibly joined by Safety, Leadtime, and Days of Inventory.

→ Line rebalancing charts showing takt time, and with magnetic strips for each work element, kept in the team area.

→ Keep teams informed of new products and developments by progress boards, including Gantt charts.

→ Men / People: A skills matrix is becoming well established - fill in the quadrants of a circle to indicate achievement from beginner to instructor.

→ Employee suggestions and employee of the month are more common in service than manufacturing - why?

→ Have a mirror with a slogan such as "You are looking at our most important source of ideas"

→ Methods: Keep those standards and methods at the workplace!

→ Materials: Don't forget to keep footprinting up to date. Kanban remains the most visible effective means for production control. Display the schedule.

→ Maintenance: A maintenance "red tag" board, showing all outstanding concerns.

→ Money: There is a welcome tendency towards displaying company financial and sales data on the shop floor.

→ Improvement: Keep a flipchart handy to note problems (which accumulate Pareto style) and suggestions with stage reached shown by filled in quadrant (suggested, investigated, being implemented, solved).

→ Storyboards, showing the stages of improvement, often using the "7 Tools" of Quality are a great motivator and training aid.

→ 5S: Display area responsibilities and 5-minute cleanup plans. Use shadowboards. Label and organise. Use kitchen organisation, not garage organisation. Display audit results and winners.

Audio is also useful. At Toyota each robot cell has its own unique tune, which gets played over loudspeaker when there is a stoppage or problem. Maintenance engineers learn to listen out for the tunes they are responsible for. At Ford, pagers are used.

Galsworth suggests appointing a "visual co-ordinator", and a management champion, who encourage and monitor the status of visual management in a plant. She makes the important points that visual management extends beyond the shop floor to the design of forms, to the presentation of information, to office layout, and to the home, together saving countless hours of waste spent searching and clarifying.

FURTHER READING:

Michel Grief, *The Visual Factory,* Productivity, Portland, OR, 1991, ISBN 0-915299-67-4
Gwendolyn Galsworth, *Visual Systems: Harnessing the Power of a Visual Workplace,* AmaCom, New York, 1997

POINT OF PRODUCTION CONTROL

Point of Production (PoP) control systems are visual, automatic real time displays, used at the point of production. They may be used as an alternative or supplement to kanban, or to monitor production progress, or tool or inventory usage. A PoP system is usually an electronic display board linked to a production process that provides continuous, automatic, and real-time monitoring. The display should be located at the workplace, as the name suggests, but the display may be duplicated in other locations such as a production control office or maintenance centre. Of course, in lean operations it is common to record and display information lineside (which is good), but such displays are usually not PoPs since they are not automatic, continuous and real time.

What a PoP has in common with a Pokayoke is that monitoring is automatic, but a PoP does not test or take action.

An example of a PoP is Toyota's line stop clock that shows the accumulated time that the assembly line has been stopped for during a shift. This display is located on the shop floor and in the production control office. At Toyota, the reason for the line stoppage is also recorded on a PC system, so as to establish Pareto priorities for continuous improvement focus. Further common examples are a display showing the number of parts made on a press, the changeover stoppage time, a load cell monitoring the number of parts, and the number of cuts made by a tool (linked to a TPM system), time in a cell, or time waiting before being moved. All of these examples are automatic, requiring no operator data entry and all may be linked to PC systems which can take automatic actions such as ordering parts or scheduling maintenance. This up-to-the-second control is an appropriate use of computers in a lean plant, vastly more effective than the humorous time estimates produced on manual MRP.

Of course, such systems have been in use in the process industry for many years. The number of possibilities is limited only by the imagination of engineers and operators.

ELECTRONIC PoP: THE NEW POKAYOKE

At GM's Saturn plant a Windows NT-based system continuously monitors 120,000 data points. A "dispatcher" controls the system and sends appropriate maintenance and other staff to any problem that might occur. This system is part of an intranet that allows employees to log on and analyse quality and production problems. The display shows a 3-D model of the car. Common data is available to everyone operators to product engineers to managers. The system has been responsible for a radical chance in the work life of operators at the plant who were already organised in self directed work teams.

REFERENCE:
Bill Gates and Collins Hemmingway, *Business @ the Speed of Thought,* Warner Books, New York, 1999

GOLDRATT

➡ Throughput, inventory, operating expense
➡ Dependent events, statistical fluctuation
➡ Constraints, bottlenecks and the synchronous rules
➡ Drum, buffer, rope
➡ Theory of constraints and thinking process

GOLDRATT

This section deals with the remarkable contributions of Eli Goldratt. Sometimes the Goldratt ideas have been seen as being in conflict to Lean operations. In fact, there is remarkable synergy. Possibly the only real conflict is in the use of OPT, black-box type, software rather than JIT style visual control. (OPT was the computer based finite scheduling package originally developed by Goldratt, but now owned by STG). In particular the Theory of Constraints (TOC) principles, which have developed from OPT, have been used by many successful lean organisations, even though they do not use the software.

In an excellent paper, Moore and Schienkopf explain the synergy between TOC and Lean. TOC is able to identify the constraints that Lean is then able to target for waste reduction. Both are logical and pragmatic. Both share the goal of flow and throughput. TOC is better at identifying that handful of potential improvements that will make a real difference. Lean has a battery of useful tools and an attractive philosophy. Lean's mapping techniques enable one to understand the system and its dependencies more clearly. TOC helps to identify and quantify the opportunities without taking the "leap of faith" sometimes associated with some lean implementations. Both encourage pull rather than push. But in some circumstances, for example where demand is erratic, the "drum buffer rope" may be more effective than kanban.

THROUGHPUT, INVENTORY, OPERATING EXPENSE

Goldratt advocates the use of Throughput ("the rate at which the system generates money through sales"), Inventory ("the money invested in purchasing things that it intends to sell"), and Operating Expense ("the money that the system spends to turn inventory into throughput") as the most appropriate measures for the flow of material. We should note some important differences with more conventional usage of these words. Throughput is the volume of sales in money terms, not units. Some constraint or bottleneck, either internal or external governs this. Inventory is the basic cost of materials used and excludes value added for work in progress. Just building inventory is of no use unless it is sold, so its value should not be recorded until it is sold. And Operating Expense makes no distinction between direct and indirect costs, which is seen as a meaningless distinction. The aim, of course, is to move throughput up, and inventory and operating expense down. Any investment should be judged on these criteria alone. This cuts decision making to the bone.

DEPENDENT EVENTS AND STATISTICAL FLUCTUATIONS

Goldratt believes that pure, uninterrupted flow in manufacturing is rare if not impossible. This is because of what he terms "statistical fluctuation" - the minor changes in process speed, operator performance, quality of parts, and so on. Average flow rates are not good enough to calculate throughput. Goldratt has a dice game to illustrate this. Each round, five operators roll a dice that represents their possible production capacity in that time period. The average of each dice roll is

3.5, so one might expect that the average production over say 20 rounds would average 3.5 units per round. In fact, this does not happen because intermediate workers are from time to time starved of parts due to the rolls of previous operators. Try it. These are dependent events. Even with very large buffer inventories between operators, part shortages sometimes develop. JIT, according to Goldratt, aims attacking statistical fluctuation so as to enable flow - so it does. But Goldratt believes that this is both very difficult and a waste of resources - which should be better directed at bottlenecks. Hence the OPT rules in the next section.

This may sound like conflict. In fact, one should take the best of both. Yes, try to reduce statistical fluctuation, but also be aware of dependent events and bottlenecks. Remember, that OPT is more applicable in batch environments that are moving towards flow manufacturing. The more you reduce changeover times, the more you smooth demand, the more you reduce variation, the more you tackle waste, the better. Irrespective of OPT, JIT, or whatever.

CONSTRAINTS, BOTTLENECKS AND NON-BOTTLENECKS: THE SYNCHRONOUS RULES

A constraint is something that prevents an enterprise from making more money, or perhaps in the case of a non-profit enterprise, something that prevents it from growing or from serving its customers better. There are four types of constraint: physical (a "bottleneck" in a plant is an example), logistical (say, response time), managerial (policy, rules), and behavioural (the activities of particular employees).

In plant scheduling, however, it is bottlenecks that determine the throughput of the plant. For many this is a whole new, radical idea. Note that what is being said is that there is generally only one bottleneck, like the weakest link in a chain. A "balanced" plant should not be the concern of management, but rather the continuing identification, exposure, and elimination of a series of bottlenecks. Eventually other constraints may be the determining factor. Examples are a market constraint or a behavioural constraint. Whilst working on the elimination of the bottleneck, the schedule should be organised around this bottleneck. The principles (often referred to as the OPT or Synchronous principles) are:

1. *Balance flow, not capacity.* For too long, according to Goldratt, the emphasis has been on trying to equate the capacity of the workcentres through which a product passes during manufacture. This is futile, because there will inevitably be faster and slower processes. So, instead, effort should be made to achieve a continuous flow of materials. This means, for example, eliminating unnecessary queues of work in front of non-bottleneck workcentres, and by splitting batches so that products can be moved ahead to the next workstation without waiting for the whole batch to be complete.
2. *The utilisation of a non-bottleneck is determined not by its own capacity but by some other constraint in the system.* A non-bottleneck should not be used all the time or overproduction will result, and therefore the capacity and utilisation of non-bottlenecks is mostly irrelevant. (Traditional accountants have choked on this one!). It is the bottlenecks that should govern flow.
3. *Utilisation and Activation are not synonymous.* This emphasises the point that a non-bottleneck machine should not be "activated" all the time because overproduction will result. Activation is only effective if the machine is producing at a balanced rate; and this is called utilisation. Notice that this differs from the conventional definition of utilisation, which ignores capacity of the bottleneck.
4. *An hour lost at a bottleneck is an hour lost for the whole system.* Since a bottleneck governs the amount of throughput in a factory, if the bottleneck stops it is equivalent to stopping the entire factory. The implications of this for maintenance, scheduling, safety stocks, and selection of equipment are profound! If you think about this, it also has deeply significant implications for cost accounting.

5. *An hour saved at a non-bottleneck is merely a mirage.* In effect it is worthless. This also has implications for the areas mentioned in point 4.

6. *Bottlenecks govern both throughput and inventory in the system.* A plant's output is the same as the bottleneck's output, and inventory should only be let into a factory at a rate that the bottleneck is capable of handling.

7. *The transfer batch may not, and many times should not, equal the process batch.* A transfer batch is the amount of work in process inventory that is moved along between workstations. Goldratt is saying that this quantity should not necessarily equal the production batch quantity that is made all together. Instead batch splitting should be adopted to maintain flow and minimise inventory cost. This applies particularly to products that have been already processed on bottleneck machines - they are then too valuable to have to wait for the whole batch to be complete. Note that MRP makes an assumption at odds with this principle, in assuming that batches will always be kept together.

8. *The process batch should be variable, not fixed.* The optimal schedule cannot, or should not, be constrained by the artificial requirement that a product must be made in one large batch. It will often be preferable to split batches into sub-batches. On bottleneck machines, batches should be made as large as possible between setup (changeover) operations (thereby minimising setup time) but on non-bottlenecks, batches should be made as small as possible by setting up machines as often as possible so as to use all the time available. What is being suggested is the fairly radical view that batches not being processed on bottlenecks should be split, and the machine re-set up for other product batches, to such an extent that the non-bottlenecks become near-bottlenecks.

9. *Lead times are the result of a schedule, and cannot be predetermined.* Here Goldratt disagrees with the use of standard pre-specified lead times such as one usually finds in MRP.

10. *Schedules should be assembled by looking at all constraints simultaneously.* In a typical factory, some products will be constrained by production capacity, others by marketing, and yet others perhaps by management inaction. It is important to know which constraints are affecting performance in any part of an enterprise. If, for example, you have a production constraint, it would be foolish to expend more effort on marketing.

The thought that a bottleneck governs throughput of a plant has massive implications for investment, costing, and continuous improvement. Essentially, an investment that only affects a non-bottleneck is waste. Likewise, continuous improvement efforts. Recall that decisions should be based upon the impact on throughput, inventory, and operating expense.

Costing has also had a shake-up. "Throughput accounting" uses the equation Revenue - direct materials - operating expenses = Profit. Here, there is no "variable overhead", direct labour is not subtracted when calculating throughput and is treated as a fixed (or temporarily fixed) cost, and inventories are not revalued on their path through the plant. Therefore, throughput accounting is simpler and more meaningful.

DRUM, BUFFER, ROPE

According to the Goldratt philosophy, the Drum, Buffer, and Rope principle should govern all plants. The drum is the beat of the bottleneck that determines the throughput. A time buffer (meaning a buffer representing so many hours of the next items to be processed, rather than a number of items). And the imaginary rope links the bottleneck with the gateway or entrance work-centres, like a long-distance kanban. The rate of entry of work into the system is thereby synchronised with the bottleneck-processing rate; if the bottleneck should stop, no more work is let into the system.

This suggests that the schedule should be built around the bottleneck. Forward schedule on the bottleneck, and backward schedule on non-bottlenecks. Then combine with the synchronous rules. This is not necessarily a simple thing to do.

Goldratt used a hiking analogy in his book The Goal to illustrate Drum Buffer Rope, Dependent Events and Statistical Fluctuations. Initially fat Herbie, carrying a heavy pack, brings up the rear and is left behind on the trail. The others beat him to the campsite. But what is important is not when the first hiker gets to camp, but the last hiker, who also carries vital equipment, arrives. So the hikers decide to put Herbie towards the front, since those following can easily catch up any time that Herbie loses. They also offload his pack as much as possible. Herbie, of course, is the bottleneck. Then the hikers go one step further. A rope is attached from Herbie to the person in the lead on the trail to prevent him getting too far ahead. But the rope also has some slack to allow for fluctuations. By the way, because of fluctuations and dependent events, this system works best if the slowest walker is significantly slower than the others.

THEORY OF CONSTRAINTS AND THINKING PROCESS.

Theory of Constraints (TOC) and the related Thinking Process (TP) was and is being developed by Eli Goldratt as an extension to his classic work The Goal. Goldratt claims wide applicability for TOC, not limited to manufacturing management. As a physicist, Goldratt has developed TOC / TP along rigorous formal lines with numerous tests and validation steps. Because of this, TOC is by no means simple to get into, nor is a "quick and dirty" form of analysis.

At the heart of TOC is the realisation that if a company had no constraints it would make an infinite profit. Most companies have a very small number of true constraints. From this follows Goldratt's five step TOC process of ongoing improvement:

1. Identify the constraint or constraints.
2. Decide how to "exploit" the constraints. A constraint is precious, so don't waste it. If it is a production bottleneck, make sure you keep it going, protect it with a time buffer, seek alternative routings, don't process defectives on it, make it quality capable, ensure it has good maintenance attention, ensure that only parts for which there is a confirmed market in the near future are made on it.
3. "Subordinate" all other resources to the constraint. This means giving priority to the constraint over all other resources. Make everyone aware of the constraint's importance. For instance move inventory in small batches after processing on the constraint, give priority to changeover on the constraint, schedule the plant around the constraint, etc.
4. "Elevate" the constraint. Only after doing steps 2 and 3, get more capacity from the constraint. Buy an additional machine or work overtime on the constraint.
5. Finally, if the constraint has been broken, go to step 1. Otherwise continue. Be careful that you do not make inertia the new constraint, by doing nothing.

One problem is how to identify the constraints; another is bringing about the necessary change. This is where the Thinking Process comes in. Here, only an overview is attempted and the reader is recommended to read the excellent guide by Dettner or to attend one of the courses offered by the Goldratt Institute.

Although many manufacturing problems occur on the shop floor (and may be amenable to analysis by other techniques developed by Goldratt), eventually the constraint falls outside the shop floor in (say) marketing or human resources, and more commonly in interdisciplinary areas. Goldratt believes that there are three questions fundamental to change. For each, Goldratt has developed one or more tools.

The three questions and their corresponding thinking process (TP) tools are:

What to Change?

"Current Reality Tree": to identify root causes or core problems

What to Change To?

"Evaporating Cloud": to expose current conflicts and to break deadlocks
"Future Reality Tree: to check if the "injection" developed in the Evaporating Cloud will eliminate the symptoms

How to Change?

"Prerequisite Tree": to identify the obstacles to change
"Transition Tree": to identify the specific actions needed for change.

The Thinking Process tools can be used in sequence or stand-alone. For instance, several manufacturing managers and consultants (in the author's experience) find the Evaporating Cloud very useful, make occasional use of the Current Reality Tree, but very rarely use the other tools.

There are a number of conventions used in drawing Thinking Process diagrams, and the reader is advised to become familiar with these in the Dettner reference

A brief overview of some of the Thinking Process tools follows:

CURRENT REALITY TREE

The Current Reality Tree begins by collecting (brainstorming? interviews?) a list of symptoms of "undesirable effects" (UDEs) - usually between 5 and 10. The next step is to connect any UDEs that appear to be causally related. (Beware, however: each connection needs to be "scrutinised" using Goldratt's "Categories of Legitimate Reservation", using an outside validator (a neutral third party). The potential relationship should be stated as "if A then B". The validator may express a legitimate reservation, from a list of tests.

Then, proceed to connect all other UDEs, once again scrutinising the links. Stop when all have been connected. Then read the diagram from the bottom up, once again scrutinising. Expand or trim the tree if necessary. Finally, identify the point of entry which contributes to most UDEs (at least to 70% either directly or indirectly is considered satisfactory). An example is given on the next page.

Example.
By interviewing various shop floor managers, the following list of UDEs was developed:
1. Lead times are long
2. External schedules are not smooth
3. Materials handling distances are excessive
4. Rework is high
5. Setups are too long
6. Welding processes are not consistent
7. Parts are pushed in batches
8. Layout is poor
9. Internal schedules are not consistent
   and, later
10. Improvement is not practised

In the example the nine UDEs were collected by interview, and a tenth added during analysis. This turns out to be a root cause. Note however, that although the root cause should be tackled as a priority, the next level of actions is also apparent.

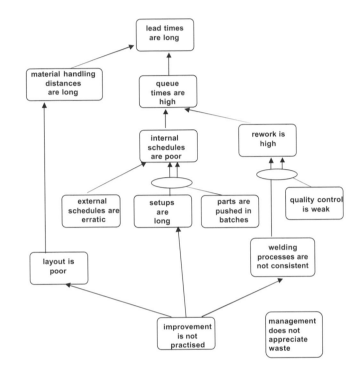

EVAPORATING CLOUDS

Goldratt believes that most core, real-world problems are intuitively recognised, but that their solution involves compromise. For instance, you can go on improving a design, but this takes time; hence there is a compromise between the designers wish for technical optimality, and the marketers wish to sell the product. If no compromise is necessary, there is no problem and it can immediately be done. The Evaporating Cloud method does not strive to reach the compromise, but rather it concentrates on invalidating the problem itself.

The standard form of the evaporating cloud is shown in the figure. Note that it is written down from left to right, beginning with the objective or constraint that is preventing progress written in. This can be obtained directly from the analysis undertaken in the Current Reality Tree. Then, the Requirements for the objective to happen are discussed and written in. Thereafter the prerequisites for the requirements to be true are determined. These are necessarily in conflict; otherwise there is no barrier to implementation.

The technique brings out the logical connections. To quote Goldratt: "one of the most basic fundamentals of logic is that behind any logical connection there is an assumption. ... The Evaporating Cloud technique is based upon verbalising the assumptions hidden behind the arrows, forcing them out and challenging them. It's enough to invalidate even one of these assumptions, no matter which one, and the problem collapses, disappears." (Goldratt, Theory of Constraints, pp 44-48).

In the example, the intervention is to introduce a quantified evaluation method which will enable operators to evaluate improvements quickly and thus to demonstrate to management the cost of waste and the opportunities to be gained. The payback is immediately apparent, as is the contribution of the operators.

One might think that this solution could have been arrived at directly, without going through all the previous stages. Often, however, obvious solutions are only obvious in retrospect. The point is, the right problem has been identified together with an appropriate course of action.

THE OTHER TP TOOLS

The remaining three techniques of the thinking process will not be described here. Suffice it to say that they use a similar methodology and the standard symbols. They are time consuming, but worthwhile in as far as they improve the chance of implementation success - something that is sadly lacking in most analytical techniques. They are a weapon against "muddling through".

(Note: Dealing with such "messy" real-world problems may also be tackled through Soft Systems Methodology - see separate section. This too is a rigorous approach when properly applied. It may possible to combine the two).

FURTHER READING:

H. William Dettner, *Goldratt's Theory of Constraints: A Systems Approach to Continuous Improvement,* ASQC Quality Press, Milwaukee WI, 1997, ISBN 0-87389-370-0

Eli Goldratt, *The Theory of Constraints,* North River Press, New York, 1990.

Robert E Stein, *The Theory of Constraints: Applications in Quality and Manufacturing,* (Second edition, Revised and expanded), Marcel Dekker, New York, 1997

Mokshagundam Srikanth and Harold Cavallaro, *Regaining Competitiveness: Putting The Goal to Work,* (Second Revised Edition), North River Press, Great Barrington, MA, 1993

Eric Noreen, Debra Smith and James Mackey, *The Theory of Constraints and its Implications for Management Accounting,* North River Press, Great Barrington, MA, 1995

Richard Moore and Lisa Schienkopf, *Theory of Constraints and Lean Manufacturing Friends or Foes?,* Chesapeake Consulting Inc., 1998 (Supplied by Goldratt Institute).

The Goldratt Institute:

Avraham Y. Goldratt (UK) Ltd, Oldfield Lodge, 156 Bridge Road, Maidenhead, SL6 8DG, Telephone 01633 278035

QUALITY

→ The Kano Model
→ Failsafing (Pokayoke)
→ Short Run SPC
→ Precontrol

THE KANO MODEL

Dr. Noriaki Kano is a Japanese quality expert who is best known for his excellent "Kano model". The Kano Model has emerged as one the most useful and powerful aids to product and service design and improvement available. It is included here because of its relevance to QFD, the design process and R&D.

The Kano model relates three factors (which Kano argues are present in every product or service) to their degree of implementation or level of implementation, as shown in the diagram. Kano's three factors are Basic (or "must be") factors, Performance (or "more is better") factors, and Delighter (or "excitement") factors. The degree of customer satisfaction ranges from "disgust", through neutrality, to "delight".

THE KANO MODEL

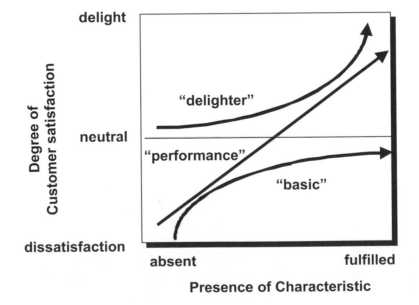

To test if a characteristic is basic, performance or delighter, ask two questions :
1. how do you feel if (the characteristic) is absent ?
2. how do you feel if (the characteristic) is present ?

if 1 = bad, 2 = neutral, it is a basic
if 1=neutral, 2 = good, it is a delighter
if the answer is "it depends", it is a performance

A Basic factor is something that a customer simply expects to be there. If it is not present the customer will be dissatisfied or disgusted, but if it is fully implemented or present it will merely result in a feeling of neutrality. Examples are clean sheets in a hotel, a station tuner on a radio, or windscreen washers on a car. Notice that there may be degrees of implementation: sheets may be clean but blemished. Basic factors should not be taken for granted, or regarded as easy to satisfy; some may even be exceptionally difficult to identify. One example is course handouts that a lecturer may regard as trivial but the audience may regard as a basic necessity. If you don't get the basics right, all else may fail - in this respect it is like Maslow's Hierarchy of Needs: it is no good thinking about self esteem needs unless survival needs are catered for. Market research is of limited value for basics (because they are simply expected). Therefore a designer needs to build up a list by experience, observation and organised feedback.

A Performance factor can cause disgust at one extreme, but if fully implemented can result in delight. This factor is also termed "more is better" but could also be "faster is better" or "easier is better". Performance factors are usually in existence already, but are neutral, causing neither disgust nor delight. It is not so much the fact that the feature exists, it is how it can be improved. The challenge is to identify them, and to change their performance. Examples are speed of check in at a hotel, ease of tuning on a radio, or fuel consumption. Performance factors represent real opportunity to designers and to R&D staff. They may be identified through market research, but observation is also important, especially to identify performance features that is causing dissatisfaction. Creativity or process redesign is often required to deliver the factor faster or easier, and information support may play a role as in the "one minute" check-in at some top hotels. The Cycle of Service (see separate section) is a useful starting point to identify performance factors.

Finally, a Delighter is something that customers do not expect, but if present may cause increasing delight. Examples are flowers and wine awaiting guest arrivals in some hotel rooms, or a radio tuner that retunes itself when moving out of range of a transmitter. By definition, market research is of little use here. Once again, it is creativity, based on an appreciation of (latent) customer needs that can provide the breakthrough.

We should also note that the Kano factors are not static. What may be a Delighter this year may migrate towards being a basic in a few years time. And also, what may be a Delighter in one part of the world may be a basic in another. Thus it is crucial to keep up to date with changing customer expectations. Benchmarking may be a way to go. From Kano we also learn that a reactive quality policy, reacting to complaints, or dissatisfiers, will at best lead to neutrality but proactive action is required to create delight. As Schneider and Bowen state, "if you dissatisfy customers by not meeting their expectations you can still recover", but "if you dissatisfy customers by not meeting their basic needs you will lose them". In a time when customer retention is increasingly important to profitability, the Kano concepts are therefore key.

The Kano Model works well with Quality Function Deployment. Basics should be satisfied, and delighters can be explicitly traded off in the "roof" of the QFD matrix (for example fuel consumption may suggest a lighter car, but safety a stronger one - so the quest is to find material that is light, strong, and inexpensive.)

FURTHER READING:
Unfortunately readings in English are difficult to obtain, but an excellent article is Hofmeister, Walters, Gongos, "Discovering Customer WOW's", *Annual Quality Congress,* ASQC, May 1996, pp759-770
Lou Cohen, *Quality Function Deployment,* Addison Wesley, Reading MA, 1995, pp 36-41

Failsafing (Pokayoke)

The late Shigeo Shingo did not invent failsafing ("pokayoke" in Japanese, literally mistake proofing), but developed and classified the concept, particularly in manufacturing. More recently failsafing in services has developed. Shingo's book *Zero Quality Control: Source Inspection and the Pokayoke System* is the classic work.

A failsafing device is a simple, often inexpensive, device that literally prevents defects from being made. The characteristics of a failsafing device are that it undertakes 100% automatic inspection (a true pokayoke would not rely on human memory or action), and either stops or gives warning when a defect is discovered. Note that a pokayoke is not a control device like a thermostat or toilet control valve that takes action every time, but rather a device that senses abnormalities and takes action only when an abnormality is identified.

Shingo distinguishes between "mistakes" (which are inevitable) and "defects" (which result when a mistake reaches a customer.). The aim of pokayoke is to design devices that prevent mistakes becoming defects. Shingo also saw quality control as a hierarchy of effectiveness from "judgement inspection" (where inspectors inspect), to "informative inspection" where information is used to control the process as in SPC, and "source inspection" which aims at checking operating conditions "before the fact". Good pokayokes fall into this last category.

According to Shingo there are three types of failsafing device: "contact", "fixed value", and "motion step". This means that there are six categories, as shown in the figure with service examples.

POKAYOKE Types

	Control	Warning
Contact	Parking height bars Armrests on seats	Staff mirrors Shop entrance bell
Fixed Value	French fry scoop Pre-dosed medication	Trays with indentations
Motion Step	Airline lavatory doors	Spellcheckers Beepers on ATMs

after: Failsafe Services :
Richard Chase and Douglas Stewart, OMA Conference, 1993

The contact type makes contact with every product or has a physical shape that inhibits mistakes. An example is a fixed diameter hole through which all products must fall; an oversize product does not fall through and a defect is registered. The fixed value method is a design that makes it clear when a part is missing or not used. An example is an "egg tray" used for the supply of parts. Sometimes this type can be combined with the contact type, where parts not only have to be present in the egg tray but also are automatically correctly aligned. The motion step type automatically ensures that the correct number of steps have been taken. For example, an operator is required to step on a pressure-sensitive pad during every assembly cycle, or a medicine bottle has a press-down-and-turn feature for safety. Other examples are a checklist, or a correct sequence for switches that do not work unless the order is correct.

Shingo further developed failsafe classification by saying that there are five areas (in manufacturing) that have potential for failsafing: the operator (Me), the Material, the Machine, the Method, and the Information (4 M plus I). An alternative is the process control model comprising input, process, output, feedback, and result. All are candidates for failsafing. According to Grout, areas where pokayoke should be considered include areas where worker vigilance is required, where mispositioning is likely, where SPC is difficult, where external failure costs dramatically exceed internal failure costs, and in mixed model and JIT production.

Shingo says that pokayoke should be thought of as having both a short action cycle (where immediate shut down or warning is given), but also a long action cycle where the reasons for the defect occurring in the first place are investigated. John Grout makes the useful point that one drawback of pokayoke devices is that potentially valuable information about process variance may be lost, thereby inhibiting improvement.

FURTHER READING:

Shigeo Shingo, *Zero Quality Control: Source Inspection and the Pokayoke System,* Productivity Press, 1986

WEB SITES:

An impressive site with numerous examples and pictures is at:
http://www.cox.smu.edu/jgrout/poke-yoke.html

Short Run SPC

Traditional SPC has been around for 60 years or more, but really relies on longer production runs on which samples of say minimum 20 can be based. This assumption does not fit easily with Lean thinking or JIT, where short runs are the order of the day. Although it is possible to maintain separate control charts for each product group using a process, short run SPC is far more efficient. A "short run" is a situation where there is limited data available to calculate control limits. (Traditional SPC is dealt with in the companion publication *The Quality 60,* as are the other "7 tools" of Quality. Apart from traditional SPC, the other 7 tools are valid and useful for both lean and traditional operations, and should be known by every manager.) Short run SPC is ideally suited to mixed model production.

A short run control chart uses the same type of mean and range chart (X bar and R chart) as in standard SPC, except that all readings have to be standardised or made "unitless". By standardising the points, a short run chart allows different parts from a single process to be controlled on the same control chart. This makes it ideal for short runs and mixed model production. The mathematical derivation of the short run formulas is given in the references.

The standardised control limits, used for all short run charts, are as follows:

UCL individuals = +A2   UCL range = D4
LCL individuals = - A2   LCL range = D3
(centreline at zero)   (centreline at 1.00)

The values of A and D are exactly those use in standard SPC, and depend upon the sample size or number of readings. Values are given in the following table :

Sample Size	A2	D3	D4
3	1.023	0	2.575
4	0.729	0	2.282
5	0.577	0	2.004
6	0.483	0	2.004

This establishes the standard control limits for each chart. Points Z are plotted on the individuals chart, and points W are plotted on the range chart. The formulas are as follows:

$$Z = \frac{Xia - Target\ Xa}{Target\ Ra} \qquad W = \frac{biggest - smallest\ value\ in\ the\ sample}{Target\ Ra}$$

where

Xia is the mean of sample i for a particular model or product a,

and

Target Xa is the target or expected average for product a. This is the "average of the averages" i.e. the average of the sample averages (x double bar). It may be obtained from previous averaged data or from midpoint of tolerance.

Target Ra is the target or estimated range of product a. This is the "average of the ranges" (R bar). It may be obtained from previous control charts, or from sampling data.

So if you have a set of products a, b, c, d that are all run through the same machine you can use the same control chart to control all four products even though each may have different expected mean and range values. Instead of four charts you need only one to detect out of control conditions on the one machine.

Once the control charts have been set up, and points have begun to be plotted on the individual and range charts, all the rules for "out of control" conditions applicable to normal SPC charts apply. For instance, any single point beyond the control limit of either chart, 7 successive values above the centre line. Often, out of control criteria will be detected automatically where the charts are maintained on computer. Also, and importantly, control chart interpretation (e.g. trend, freaks, shift, etc.) also applies. A full diagram can be found in *The Quality 60.*

A nice feature of short run SPC charts is that they can be set up in advance, and the same chart used when new products are added or old products dropped. All you need to know or estimate is the target average value and the target range value.

Another method for short run control is given in the next section.

FURTHER READING:

Stephen A Wise and Douglas C Fair, *Innovative Control Charting,* ASQ Press, Milwaukee, WI, 1998, ISBN 0-87389-385-9, Chapter 15

John Bicheno, *The Quality 60,* PICSIE Books, Buckingham, 1998

PRECONTROL

Statistical Process Control (SPC) is more suited to longer production runs where a large number of samples can be taken over time. Unfortunately this is not the case with many JIT systems. Also, particularly with JIT, it is important to verify as quickly as possible if a changeover has been undertaken correctly and the process is capable of producing good quality parts. One possibility is to use Precontrol, originally developed by consultants Rath and Strong.

The procedure is as follows :

Divide the tolerance (or specification) band (i.e. the area between the upper and lower tolerance limits) into 4 equal bands. The middle two bands are the green zone (and should be coloured green on a chart). The two outer areas are called the yellow zone. Beyond the tolerance limits is the red band.

PRECONTROL CHARTS

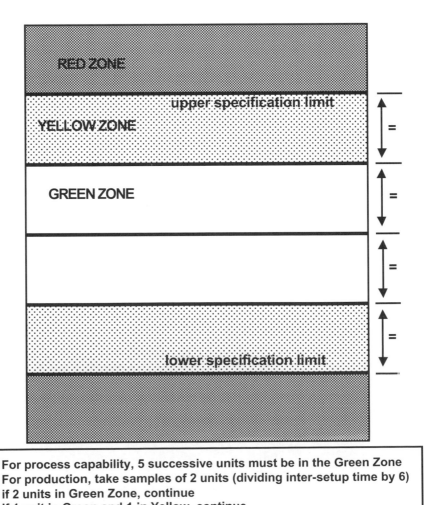

For process capability, 5 successive units must be in the Green Zone
For production, take samples of 2 units (dividing inter-setup time by 6)
if 2 units in Green Zone, continue
If 1 unit in Green and 1 in Yellow, continue
If 2 units in same Yellow zone, stop and adjust
If 2 units in opposite Yellow zones, stop
If 1 unit in a Red Zone, stop

Following Changeover (to check capability) : Measure 5 consecutive units.

➜   If all five are in the green zone, the process is in control. Production can start.

➜   If even one is in the red zone, the process is not in control. Production must not start. Reset the process.

➜   If one is in the yellow zone, a 'special cause' may be present. Take another sample of 5. Better still, investigate.

➜   If two consecutive readings fall in the yellow zone, adjust the process and restart the measurement process.

During production :

1.   Take samples of two consecutive units.
2.   If even one unit falls in the red zone, stop production and investigate. Return to Step 1.
3.   If both units fall in the yellow zones, stop production and investigate. Return to Step 1.
4.   If one unit falls in the yellow zone and one in the green, continue.
5.   If both units fall in the green, continue.

Sample 6 pairs between setups. (e.g. for an hour long batch, sample approximately every 10 minutes)

The method is obviously very simple. Precontrol charts can be printed ahead of time and no statistical training is necessary. Implementation is immediate. However, critics have pointed out that Precontrol is based on tolerance limits, not on process variation as is the case with SPC. As such the method relies on these tolerances being carefully set during design. Some statisticians have pointed out that a sample size of 2 may simply be inadequate. Nevertheless, the technique is statistically based and is likely to be reliable under many circumstances. Bhote has been a strong advocate of Precontrol, has pointed out some weaknesses in SPC, and claims that SPC is a "horse and buggy" in the Jet Age. Bhote claims that Precontrol has overtaken SPC in popularity in Japan.

REFERENCES:
Dorian and Peter Shainin, "Precontrol versus X and R Charting", *Quality Engineering*, Vol 1 No 4, 1989.
Keki R Bhote, *World Class Quality*, AMACOM/ASQC, 1991, Chapter 15.

SUPPLIERS AND DISTRIBUTION

➡ Supplier Partnerships
➡ Supplier Associations
➡ Integrated Supply

SUPPLIER PARTNERSHIPS

The concept of supplier partners developed strongly in the 1980s as a result of the movement towards just in time (JIT) manufacturing. JIT emphasises reduction in waste, shortening of lead times, improvement in quality, continuous improvement, and simplicity. These are also the goals of supplier partnership. Today supplier partnerships are found both in service and manufacturing.

The philosophy is that, through co-operation rather than confrontation, both parties benefit. It is a longer-term view, emphasising total cost rather than product price. Cost includes not only today's price of the part or product, but also its quality (defect / ppm rate), delivery reliability, the simplicity with which the transaction is processed, and the future potential for price reductions.

But partnership goes further : Long term, stable relationships are sought rather than short term, adversarial, quick advantage. The analogy of a marriage is often used. It may have its ups and downs, but commitment remains. In a partnership, contracts will be longer term to give the supplier confidence and the motivation to invest and improve. Both parties recognise that the game whereby low prices are bid and then argued up on contingencies once the contract is awarded, is wasteful and counter-productive. Instead, it may be possible for both parties to co-operate on price reduction, sharing the benefits between them. Such co-operation may be achieved through the temporary secondment of staff. (See the section on Supplier Associations).

For partnership to work, there must of necessity be few or single suppliers per part. There is not necessarily a risk of "being taken for a ride" because there is too much to loose. But there are ways around this too : having one supplier exclusively supplying a part to one plant, but another supplier exclusively supplying the same part to another plant. This spreads the risk whilst still achieving single supplier advantages. Alternatively there is the Japanese practice of cultivating several suppliers simultaneously but then awarding an exclusive contract to one supplier for a part for the life of the product, and selecting another supplier for a similar part going into another end product. The idea is to work with a few good, trusted suppliers who supply a wide range of parts. Partnership has therefore resulted in drastic reductions in many a company's supplier base. An objective is to remove the long tail of the supplier Pareto curve whereby perhaps 10% of parts are supplied by 80% of the suppliers. See the figure on the next page.

In common with Lean Thinking, partnership aims at waste reduction. Purchasing and Supply muda include multiple quotes, order acknowledgement, remittance advices, invoices, counting, repackaging, checking, returns, expediting, double handling, and of course storage.

Usually, partnership begins with a Pareto-type analysis of suppliers by cost and number of parts. Then, exploration as to how to reduce or combine sourcing begins. Supplier days are held, often annually, when company plans and objectives are explained, measures given, prizes for best performance given out, and factory tours held. For true partnership, director level meetings are held periodically, with much more frequent manager and engineer contact.

On quality, the partnership aims at zero receiving inspection and at delivery directly to the point of use. (By the way, partnership quality should talk in terms of ppm levels, not percentages.) Packaging and part orientation may be specifically designed to reduce waste. Delivery would often be subject to kanban call-off : the partner would be warned of gross requirements far out, more detailed requirements close in, but the actual sequence and timing of delivery is controlled by kanban. Many attempt this, far fewer achieve it. Both sides need to work towards schedule stability : the customer to not change his mind at the last moment, and the supplier to provide reliable delivery. (Unstable schedules ultimately cost the customer in terms of money and risk, and reduce the possibility of productivity gain at the supplier.) Sometimes, the supplier is responsible for maintaining inventory levels at a customer, called VMI (vendor managed inventory) which is increasingly found for consumables. Other times, a manufacturer may write the production schedule of the supplier. As trust builds, self-billing or reconciliation becomes possible ("we built 100 cars, so here is our cheque for the 500 tyres we must have used").

RATIONALISING THE SUPPLIER BASE

Suppliers, ranked in order of spend

Improved communication links via EDI or EPOS further enhance partnership advantages. Delivery co-operation becomes possible either through "milkrounds" (whereby small quantities are collected from several firms in an area every day, rather than from one firm once per week), or , where more work is given to one supplier, mixed loads are sent every day rather than one-product loads once per week. This improves flow and reduces inventories.

Co-operation on design is part of partnership. The manufacturer recognises the supplier's ability to design the parts that it makes, rather than simply specifying. This policy of "open specs" or "black box" specs can lead to faster, lower cost, and more up to date part supply. The partnership idea encourages the concept of a company sticking to its core business, whilst putting out non-core business.

Generally, supplier partnership makes sense for "A" and possibly "B" parts; less so for commodity items. Part criticality and risk also influence the partnership decision; you would not risk partnership with a company having poor industrial relations, or weak finances, or poor quality assurance. This means that a team approach is necessary in supplier selection. The Purchasing Officer may co-ordinate, but throughout the partnership Design would talk to their opposite number in Design, Quality to Quality, Production control to Production control, and so on.

Disadvantages ? Time, commitment, costs of establishment, risk of inappropriate choices of partner, and short term cost reduction opportunities foregone against medium term gains.

Value engineering (see separate section) is a technique that both parties may adopt for mutual advantage. VE/VA is a powerful technique for cost, quality and delivery. In advanced partnerships a "satellite plant" dedicated to a particular customer and located nearby, or "suppliers in residence" where the supplier's operation and or some of its staff are permanently located on the customer's site, may be worth consideration. Volkswagen's Brazilian plants are reported to use supplier's employees on the VW assembly line - is this the future of partnership, or a quest for flexibility?

In Japan, and increasingly in the rest of the world, supplier partnership is now expanding down from relationships with first tier suppliers, to second and even third tier. Larger firms in the car industry have been leaders, but other industries and smaller firms are following. The thought, in common with TQM, is that quality is only as good as the weakest link.

FURTHER READING:
James Womack, Daniel Jones, Daniel Roos, *The Machine that Changed the World,* Rawson Associates, New York, 1990, Chapter 6, ISBN 0-89256-350-8
Richard Schonberger and Edward Knod, *Operations Management* (Sixth Edition), Irwin, Illinois, 1997, Chapter 9, ISBN 0-07-114651-2
Hines, Peter (1994) *Creating World Class Suppliers: Unlocking mutual competitive advantage,* Pitman, London, ISBN 0-273-60300-0
Lamming, Richard (1993) *Beyond Partnership,* Prentice Hall, Hemel Hempstead, ISBN 0-13-143785-2

SUPPLIER ASSOCIATIONS

The supplier association concept is an extension of the supplier partnership concept. Supplier associations are "clubs" of suppliers who form together for mutual help and learning. Members may all supply one company, or are all from one region serving different customers. The associations seek to learn best practices from other members or to gain competitive advantage and/or productivity through co-operation. In Japan, Supplier Associations are known as kyoryoku kai.

There are three types of association : for operations (to gain cost, quality, delivery improvements), for purchasing (to gain from economies of scale), and for marketing (to gain from synergistic practices or by pooling expertise).

Peter Hines defines the former type as "a mutually benefiting group of a company's most important subcontractors brought together on a regular basis for the purpose of co-ordination and co-operation as well as (to) assist all the members (by benefiting) from the type of development associated with large Japanese assemblers : such as kaizen, just in time, kanban, U-cell production, and the achievement of zero defects."

The aims (following Hines) are :

→ to improve skills in JIT, TQM, SPC, VE/VA, CAD/CAM, Flexibility, Cost

→ to produce a uniform supply system

→ to facilitate the flow of information

→ to increase trust

→ to keep suppliers in touch with market developments

→ to enhance the reputation of the customer as a good business partner

→ to help smaller suppliers lacking specialist trainers and facilities

→ to increase the length of relations

→ to share developmental benefits

→ to provide an example to subcontractors as to how they should develop their own suppliers.

The company-sponsored variety may benefit from the parent company's expertise and resources, often given free. The regional variety simply shares resources such as training seminar costs and training materials, but also will share expertise by lending key staff experts to other member companies for short periods. The regional type may be partially funded from government, and may have a full-time facilitator. In Japan it is considered an honour to be asked to join a prestigious supplier association, as run by a major corporation.

Joint projects, assistance in areas of expertise, development of common standards, training, courses, an interchange or secondment of staff for short periods, benchmarking, hiring of consultants or trainers, factory visits within the association, joint visits to outside companies or other associations, are all common.

The type of supplier who may join an association is not necessarily dependent on size - in fact, larger suppliers with their own corporate resources may benefit less. Also, suppliers of common or catalogue parts may not be invited. Suppliers that are usually targeted are those dependent upon a parent for a significant (perhaps 25% or more) proportion of their business. The purchasing department of the parent company often plays a key role, but some supplier associations have been set up on the initiative of lower tier suppliers or academic groups (such as the Cardiff's Lean Enterprise Unit)

Often, a supplier association will hold an annual or biannual assembly to look at performance figures. Ranking of suppliers by different measure is presented. This is often sufficient motivation for lower ranking members to ask for help or to take action on their own.

A supplier association usually will have its own set of rules and regulations and be run by (perhaps) a retired senior engineer from the parent company or increasingly by a full- or part-time co-ordinator from one of the companies. Support staff are seconded for short periods, depending on projects and needs. Often member companies pay a subscription fee. At the top level, the association will have a steering group at MD level, which meets perhaps annually. Some functional directors may meet quarterly. Engineers and front line staff may meet more frequently or may form temporary full-time task groups to address particular problems. Some associations consider social events to be important icebreakers. Within the association there may be a functional split by product category, or by area of concern (cost, quality, delivery, production planning, etc.)

Purchasing Associations:

A variation is an association that bands together for mutual purchasing advantage, gaining from improved quantity discounts and greater "clout" than a single company can bring to bear. A database of required materials and goods is usually maintained, sometimes by a third party. These have been successful in Australia, often on the initiative of a purchasing consultant. A purchasing association does not necessarily go in for all the activities of an operations association, and may be confined to purchasing staff.

A type that has become fairly common in JIT plants is where a contractor takes on the responsibility for the inventory management and supply of numerous small items. This is a form of "vendor managed inventory". Because such contractors operate in different regions they may be able to gain quantity discounts some of which are passed on. Typically such a contractor supplies one large plant, but there are variations where a contractor supplies numerous small firms in a region. This is almost like having a co-operative shop, except that the contractor is a professional inventory manager and re-stocker.

A **Marketing Association** may have characteristics similar to "Agile Manufacturers". That is, they pool resources for synergistic gain or to win large contracts. Such groupings, often known as consortia, have been common in defence, computing, and construction.

Further reading:

Peter Hines, *Creating World Class Suppliers : Unlocking mutual competitive advantage,* FT/Pitman, London, 1994. ISBN 0-273-60300-0

For a case study on the establishment of a supplier association in Wales see
Dan Dimancescu, Peter Hines, Nick Rich, *The Lean Enterprise,* AmaCom, New York, 1997 , ISBN 0-8144-0365-4

INTEGRATED SUPPLY

Integrated supply is the concept of having an intermediate supplier between a large number of small suppliers and a manufacturer. Instead of dealing with numerous small suppliers, the company deals with only one intermediate supplier. This concept developed directly out of the desire to reduce the supplier base, which has been a strong theme in the 1990's.

Often integrated supply is used for C items and or commodity items, such as fasteners. It may also be used for the purchase of occasional specialist items, such as a bulk purchase of PICSIE books! The intermediate supplier gains a contract for say three years and is in turn responsible for negotiating supplies with a large range of companies. The integrated supplier may also be required to deliver JIT to the manufacturer or on a vendor managed inventory basis. Very often the integrated supplier will set up a warehouse very near to the customer's plant. For the customer plant there are several advantages including reduced inventory, reduced ordering costs, and probably better service with fewer headaches.

There are a number of issues:

→ Contracts need to be sufficiently long to allow the integrated supplier to establish hardware and relationships.

→ There needs to be trust or at least a guarantee that the manufacturer will not "go behind your back".

→ Price decreases are normally expected. There may be a cost saving sharing agreement.

→ Special arrangements need to be made where support services (backup or technical support) are required.

→ Procedures for the selection of second tier suppliers will normally have to be worked out, perhaps requiring the integrator to continue to use some existing suppliers.

PEOPLE

➡ Open Book Management
➡ Meetings, Memos and Responsibilities
➡ Change Management
➡ Ubuntu and Kyosei

OPEN BOOK MANAGEMENT

Open Book Management (OBM) is the simple but powerful concept of opening the books, and especially the cost accounting records ("the financials") to all employees. It also includes teaching employees to interpret the figures, allowing them to see the connection between their job and the bottom line results of the company, and trusting them to make good decisions with this knowledge. The open book approach is attributed to Jack Stack of the Springfield Remanufacturing Company. Stack led a management buy-out following the demise of International Harvester. It had enormous levels of debt, and was threatened with closure on a day-to-day basis. Jack Stack decided that the only way to survive was to share the business position with all employees; for them to understand the twin priorities of profit and cash flow. He did, and the company prospered mightily. Today many smaller companies and a few larger ones have adopted OBM in whole or in part.

OBM is about business literacy for all employees, (all employees are taught to read financial reports), about establishing clear "line of sight", about trust, about true empowerment, and ultimately about large gains in productivity through cutting unnecessary supervision and improvement through intelligent participation. Sound too good to be true ? or too big a risk? Perhaps, but not according to employees of OBM companies.

All employees at OBM companies are taught basic cost accounting, and know the money value of time, machines, and materials. These gives employees direct access to all information necessary to propose and evaluate continuous improvement initiatives themselves, and motivate them by showing the direct impact on the bottom line. OBM is like treating everyone in the company as a manager or partner. The results have often been amazing. Companies bogged down in unsuccessful productivity or quality campaigns have been given a new lease of life by OBM.

"Huddles" are a central feature. This is a form of team working and team briefing, but goes 360 degrees so management gets back the information. In "prehuddles" teams analyse performance (using productivity, quality and financial measures) and communicate upwards. In "main huddles" managers receive performance information, as do shop floor teams. In "post huddles" middle managers are briefed on performance objectives, and then in turn brief team leaders. So it is a form of Hoshin planning, except that it happens frequently with a cycle being completed at least weekly. This is about generating a continuous, powerful feedback loop.

Jack Stack refers to OBM as "the great game of business". He identifies three essential steps : creating a series of small wins, giving employees a sense of the big picture, and teaching the numbers (including financials). He believes that business should be fun and that gains are best made in a series of small games or wins. These wins or objectives are communicated weekly through the huddles, and are celebrated.

Stack describes what he calls the "myths of management" : that telling the truth or sharing the position or numbers is dangerous (more dangerous not to share, and we are all committed so why tell outsiders?), nice guys finish last (bosses who act like SOBs don't last), a manager has to come up with the answers (they can't; everyone has to participate), and others. So OBM represents real empowerment, not just talk.

And finally, Stack believes in sharing the gains, in creating "a company of owners". Bonus plans, Gainsharing, should be short term goals and equity participation the long-term goal. This follows, inevitably, if employees have an intimate knowledge of the financial performance. Of course, employees also share the risk of failure, but at least should be able to see failure coming and be able to take timeous and sensible decisions. If you believe that change results from necessity, there can be no more powerful force than OBM, where everyone has almost as detailed a picture of the market and financial performance as the managing director.

For John Case, an OBM author, OBM has four principles : sharing information (everyone has to know what is going on), business literacy (everyone needs to understand the numbers and to use them), empowerment (true responsibility for their own numbers), and last, a stake in the business. Case has also pointed out that many companies, Wal-Mart for example, have long shared extensive performance information, financial and otherwise, with employees. Over the past decade visitors to many lean factories, Japanese and Western, will have noticed a greater sharing of financial, sales, and performance information amongst employees. Typically this information is shown on display boards or in company newsletters. These are the fist steps to full OBM. John Case also notes that programs on JIT, TQM, and technical training provide the how, but OBM provides the why.

There are many similarities between OBM and "Kaizen Costing". See the separate later section.

A final note : Ricardo Semler of SEMCO of Brazil has a similarly, perhaps even more revolutionary approach. His book, Maverick!, created a stir when it suggested that there should be no job titles or organisation structure, that employees should be involved in all major decisions, that managers fix their own pay, that checking on expenses is a waste, and that managers should really treat their employees as adults - not just say so ! Phew ! It seems to have worked for them.

FURTHER READING:

Jack Stack with Bo Burlingham, *The Great Game of Business,* Currency Doubleday, New York, Paperback edition, 1994, ISBN 0-385-47525-X

John P Schuster, Jill Carpenter, M. Patricia Kane, *The Power of Open Book Management : Releasing the true potential of people's minds, hearts, and hands,* John Wiley, New York, 1996, ISBN, 0-471-13287-X

John Case, *Open Book Management : The Coming Business Revolution,* Harper Business, New York, 1995, ISBN 0-88730-708-6

John Case, "Opening the Books", *Harvard Business Review,* March-April 1997, pp119-127.

Ricardo Semler, *Maverick!,* Century Books, London, 1993, ISBN 0-7126-5451-8

MEETINGS, MEMOS AND RESPONSIBILITIES

This section covers three simple but vital issues, which are sometimes uncontrolled even in otherwise lean organisations.

MEETINGS

The first principle of meetings is that, if at all possible, they should be held at "Gemba". Gemba management means going to the location and using the facts, rather than sitting in a meeting room and discussing opinions. Use the "four actuals": go to the actual workplace, look at the actual objects in question, collect the actual data, and observe what is actually happening".

The second principle, adopted at Toyota in product design and development, is to have focused, short meetings on one topic only and to demand that all participants arrive fully prepared to discuss that one topic. Typically such meeting take 15 minutes. Meetings with long agendas and with participants unprepared but nevertheless keen to give their opinion on all topics, are definitely not Lean.

MEMOS

Minutes of meetings and memos should be standardised. (Standards apply in the office as well!). At Toyota, most minutes and memos use a standardised A3 sheet of paper. One side of one sheet. A non-Toyota example is given. By the way, this is an old idea possibly stemming from Joseph Juran's insistence on such brief notes during his trips to Japan in the 1950's.

Standardised Report Sheet

produced on one side of A3 paper photocopies circulated

Project Title	RACI chart	Space for text and / or calculations
Project history list and perhaps Gantt chart	Pareto, Fishbone, Data diagrams and maps	
	Drawings and Photographs	Concept, Layout, Takt time, etc
costing		Idea space

RESPONSIBILITIES: THE RACI DIAGRAM

The RACI chart is a very useful way of clarifying responsibilities. RACI is a mnemonic for Responsibility, Accountability, Consult and Inform. The figure shows an example. Notice that all necessary activities for the task or project are written as rows and the people concerned written as columns. At the right hand side the target completion date may be given.

RACI Chart

	PH	CB	DB	NR	JB	JS target
strategic review	R	A				I 7 / 8
product Pareto	A	I			R	R 14 / 8
big picture maps	A / C	I / C	R		R	I 16 / 8
detail maps	A	I	R	C	I	R 5 / 9
etc.						

R = responsible   A = accountable I = inform   C = consult

Responsibility identifies the persons who are primarily responsible for task completion. This does not mean the person has to do the task personally, but the person must ensure its completion.
Accountability identifies the process owner. The project manager. The task co-ordinator.
Consult identifies who must be consulted. A person who has a vital input into the task due to specialist knowledge or who is working on a related task.
Inform identifies people who are interested in the outcome.

(Thanks to Dave Brunt of LERC for bringing RACI to my attention.)

CHANGE MANAGEMENT

There are still arguments as to whether "change management" should be studied as a separate topic or whether it should be integrated into all areas of study. The significant argument in favour of the latter is that change in inherent in all aspects of modern business. Whatever. The following are a few pointers found to be useful in the implementation of Lean operations.

→   Change begins with vision. If there is no clear vision, change will be undirected. By contrast if a team has a clear goal, including timing and commitment, this is more powerful than all the theory and software in the world. Vision includes the ability to portray employees in their changed position.

→   "People don't resist change, they resist being changed" and "It is uncertainty that people fear more than change" both appear to be very true. So communicate. Don't fall into the trap of believing that somehow it is better not to inform.

→   From the previous point, consultation and involvement is preferable, even essential. A very useful technique is the Force Field Diagram, used by groups to brainstorm forces for and against change.

→   The reason for change must be made clear, as early as possible. Womack and Jones talk about "creating a crisis". Many senior managers, operators, unions, and manufacturing managers only really change when they absolutely have to. Timing is important.

→ Never try to elicit change by going behind people's backs. Informing some but not others. Never give incentives to some but not to others.

→ Recognise that all change impacts a system. A system is like a network. There will be knock-on effects. There will be beneficiaries and victims, winners and losers. Some will be advantaged, some will be threatened. This means that the first duty of a "change agent" is to think though the consequences.

→ There is a distribution of people's willingness to accept change. There are early adopters, reasonable adopters, late adopters, and die-hards. The late adopters will wait for a "critical mass" to be won over, before they become supporters. Therefore attaining a critical mass of converts must be the goal. Die-hards may have to go.

→ The stages trough which change often proceeds moves from "unconscious ignorance" to "conscious ignorance" (we know we don't know) to "conscious knowledge" to "unconscious knowledge". Another model is "unfreeze", "change", "refreeze". These stages require different tactics.

→ The transition to the new way often has to pass through a period of loss of productivity. This means managers have to "hang in there" and not "pull the plug" too early.

→ Putting people in the shoes of the customer, either internal or external, is a good tactic.

→ Gemba!

Remember the wise words of Lao Tzu, in *The Art of War*, "Go to the people. Live amongst them. Start with what they have. Build on what they know. And when the deed is done, the mission accomplished, of the best leaders the people will say 'We have done it ourselves'".

UBUNTU AND KYOSEI

This section is a bit of fun, not necessarily connected directly with lean operations. It is included because

→ the author of this publication is South African, and

→ the phrases reflect the spirit of lean enterprise.

Ubuntu is a word used in South African management circles to mean the fusion of modern management with tribal thinking. In an African tribe there is a hierarchy, but anyone may speak and will be listened to sympathetically in the knowledge that anyone can have good ideas. The literal translation from the Zulu is to do with dignity and humanity, or "a person becomes a person through other persons" or "I am because we are". In tribal societies there is the concept of the extended family with mutual help being given between age groups and between immediate family groupings. In South Africa, Ubuntu has come to mean a more people-oriented approach. It is a team-based approach to management; we are all in this together. So, "that's not Ubuntu" means it does not suit the aspirations of all; it does not fit in with the common good, it may suit the management and may even be the optimal economic thing to do, but some will be harmed. This is in line with, or should be in line with, JIT or Lean Thinking. It's a good sentiment, and about time some lean thinking came out of Africa.

Although at times a little confused about JIT, TPM, TQM and so forth, Mbigi argues for an inclusive approach towards productivity and performance. This includes developing peoples' capacity (through collective learning and creating an awareness of survival issues), reforming work (including team working, participation, as well as adoption of best practices), and reforming political and social issues (including governance, power, economic justice and fairness).

In a similar vein, Kyosei, means to work together in a spirit of co-operation for the common good, of employees, of customers, of all people, of the environment. It is a word that has become associated with the Canon Company and the Canon Production System. According to Ryuzaburo Kaku, ex president of Canon, it is like a pyramid. At the base is economic survival. Then comes co-operation with labour, and then co-operation outside the company, with customers and suppliers. Following these comes "global activism" when the company starts international operations and cooperates internationally and responsibly with foreign employees, people, and environmentally friendly technology, and lastly the company works with and uses its influence with governments around the world to act responsibly.

Too philosophical? Perhaps. But good lean thinking, perhaps even Agile.

References:

Ryuzaburo Kaku, "The Path of Kyosei", *Harvard Business Review,* July-August 1997, pp55-63
Lovemore Mbigi, *Ubuntu: The African Dream in Management,* Knowledge Resources, Pretoria, 1997, ISBN 1-874997-14-4

MEASUREMENT

➡ Management Accounting and Activity Based Costing
➡ Kaizen Costing and Pseudo Profit Centres
➡ Performance Measurement and the Balanced Scorecard
➡ Productivity Accounting

MANAGEMENT ACCOUNTING AND ACTIVITY BASED COSTING

Ansari et al have pointed out four difference between accounting systems in mass or traditional and lean environments:

→ Mass accountants assume that costs vary with inputs such as material or are fixed over a certain time period. This leads to encouraging long production runs. Lean accountants realise that volume is not necessarily the major factor, and that there are other drivers such as changeovers, OEE, and orders placed.

→ Mass accountants stress individual and departmental accountability. Lean accountants put more emphasis on teamwork and the supply chain, and try to build in team incentives.

→ Mass accountants are very much concerned with inventory costing and control. Lean accountants stress simplicity and less inventory

→ Mass accountants study and report extensively on labour. Lean accountants are more interested in indirect costs.

OVERHEAD ALLOCATION AND ABC

One reason why conventional or mass costing systems have run into trouble with modern manufacturing is that overhead costs are allocated in sometimes-inappropriate ways, resulting in misleading product costs. Mass cost accounting allocates overhead to products by a two stage process: overhead costs are allocated to cost centres or departments, and are then reallocated from cost centres to products on the basis of (typically) labour hours or machine hours consumed by the product. When direct costs were a major proportion of total costs, this made sense. Today, however, overheads form the major proportion of costs, and direct labour and machine hours very little. Major distortions are possible, even likely. Mass costing usually uses a uniform cost centre rate to distribute costs. Kaplan and Cooper tell the story of two theoretical plants, Complex Factory and Simple Factory. They both make pencils in the same annual volume, but Simple makes only one variant whilst Complex makes a huge variety. As a result Complex has far higher overheads. Since the process is the same, cost accounting would allocate costs evenly between all variants. But clearly, those low volume unusual colours actually cost a whole lot more. So complex variants are undercosted whilst standard variants are overcosted. If this persists, and if pricing is based on cost, Complex can be driven out of business. Simple, however, has no real need for another accounting system - conventional costing works well; Activity Based Costing is not needed.

Before getting into a complex overhead allocation technique such as Activity Based Costing (ABC), consider the simple but radical suggestion made by John Darlington of STG: Allocate overheads on the basis of time spent in the factory. In today's manufacturing environment this makes a lot of sense. The great thing is that it would cause many accountants to put on "lean spectacles". There would be strong incentives not to overproduce and to shift that old warehouse inventory.

Under ABC the concept is that cost elements are allocated to activities which are in turn allocated to products via "cost drivers" (i.e. the quantity of that activity consumed, such as the number of inspection activities.) Direct costs elements such as raw materials and direct labour should be allocated directly to products.

An activity-traceable cost element is the most basic cost grouping in ABC. Examples are salaries, rent, office machines, and power. A primary activity is a defined, repetitive operation that is undertaken in the company - such as planning, storage, materials handling, inspecting, receiving, shipping, accounting - which is directly linked to the value adding stream. Secondary activities, such as personnel or training, support the primary activities and their costs should be recovered via the primary activities that they serve. Cost drivers are measures relating to the volume of an activity - for instance, the number of setups made, or the area of floor space used in storage. Or, even take Darlington's suggestion of leadtime. Minor cost categories are non-traceable costs such as library and postage that are difficult to trace to particular activities and can be allocated via a conventional rule such as direct machine hours.

The unit cost per activity is determined by dividing the total cost of the activity by the volume of the activity (for example the cost per inspection). These are the cost drivers that are "consumed" by the products. Since activities are not costed in conventional systems. ABC yields valuable insight into the underlying cost structure of the business even before product costs are calculated.

So the ABC process involves the following steps :

➔ Define the cost elements (see examples above)

➔ Determine which cost elements are direct, activity traceable, and non-traceable

➔ Define appropriate primary and secondary activities to be used (not too many, nor too few ; standard lists are available, see Kaplan & Cooper p 109-110)

➔ Assemble the cost elements

➔ Allocate costs amongst primary activities

➔ Allocate costs amongst secondary activities

➔ (in doing these allocations it is useful to think of a matrix of cost elements against activities.)

➔ Apportion secondary activity costs amongst primary activities, on some appropriate basis such as hours used.

➔ Define the cost driver measures, related to the activities

➔ Determine the total volumes of the cost drivers for the accounting period

➔ Determine the unit cost per cost driver (activity cost per unit volume of activity)

➔ Measure the volume of cost driver activity consumed by each product

➔ Allocate costs to products by multiplying the appropriate unit cost drivers by the volume of the cost driver consumed by each product

➔ Add direct costs and non-traceable costs

Notice the following :

➔ ABC is more likely to yield accurate costs than conventional costing, because there is greater traceability

➔ Even with ABC, there is still considerable judgement involved, so costs are never certain

➔ ABC is a fairly complex system

→ ABC, like conventional costing, is based on assumptions about future activities which may change or whose volumes are likely not to materialise exactly. So there will still be variances

→ There is a trade-off between accuracy and complexity; one could have a complex system with scores of drivers but is all this worth it ? Better to get approximate answers faster and less expensively

If ABC is not properly used it can itself be very wasteful. It may make sense, therefore, to use it on a periodic or audit basis and not on a continual basis. You need to ask what benefit will be gained from running an ABC system continuously. Probably little.

ACTIVITY BASED MANAGEMENT

Because ABC has determined the costs of activities, this valuable information can be used in a variety of ways :

→ Knowing activity costs is valuable in itself. Activities drive product costs, and anomalies can be spotted.

→ The exercise of determining cost drivers is considered by some to be as valuable as the results obtained from ABC. The underlying cost structure may never before have been examined or debated.

→ The activities themselves may be classified as value adding, non-value adding but necessary, and non-value adding. (See the section on Lean Thinking). Now, since we have a good indication of the costs of these we can prioritise improvement activities.

→ The sensitivity of costs to changes in product mix can be assessed more accurately. This was one of the original motivations for ABC. According to Cooper and Kaplan, inappropriate costing has led to led to many of the wrong products being taken off the market, whilst not removing others that should have gone. Removing a wrong product may result in more overheads for other products that are in turn driven out.

→ "What if" analyses becomes more valuable. For instance, what if we subcontract various activities, what are the consequences of more product introductions, what if we phase out certain products ?

→ ABC is a way of looking at a company in terms of its processes rather than its departmental functions. So ABC is closely aligned with business process reengineering.

FURTHER READING:
Robert Kaplan and Robin Cooper, *Cost and Effect,* Harvard Business School Press, Boston, MA, 1998, ISBN 0-87584-788-9
P. Turney, *Common Cents : The ABC Performance Breakthrough,* Cost Technology, Portland, OR, 1992
Ernest Glad and Hugh Becker, *Activity Based Costing and Management,* Wiley, Chichester, 1996
Claudia Helberg and John Bicheno, *The Buckingham ABC Trainer,* PICSIE Books, Buckingham, 1992
Shahid Ansari et al, *Management Accounting in The Age of Lean Production,* Irwin McGraw-Hill series on Management Accounting, New York, 1997

KAIZEN COSTING AND PSEUDO PROFIT CENTRES

Kaizen costing, as the name suggests, is costing for continuous improvement. It aims to motivate operators to drive costs down, rather than to record historic costs and variances for middle manager accountability. That is a big change. So, kaizen costing is less concerned with accuracy and more concerned with putting information necessary for good decision making in the hands of the people doing the work. In this respect it has considerable overlap with open book management, OBM (see separate section).

Although it usually does relate to money, some kaizen costing does not even consider money but relates instead to productivity levels, to quality, to delivery, and to other operational figures such as absenteeism, energy used, offcut quantities, changeover times, inventory levels, and the like.

Often kaizen costing is carried out by the team itself. They are provided with the basic hourly rates (for say machines, labour, floorspace, maintenance) and other costs (materials, energy, parts) and then, following basic instruction and some help, are expected to produce (say) weekly product costs against target. The target may not be static, but may reflect (say) a 5% cost down over a 6 month horizon. The point is, in common with OBM, which by putting the responsibility for costs in the hands of operators together with information necessary to make sensible rationalisations, reflects a participative management style. Kaplan and Cooper (p61) make a number of points :

→ the idea is to motivate and inform, not to collect accurate costs.

→ the emphasis is on speed, feedback, and learning

→ it is a team responsibility : all are held collectively accountable (a feature in common with best-practice teamworking)

→ operators are expected to become involved with cost-related decision making, they are already the best qualified - now they need to be the best informed as well

→ the cost system is customised to the particular cell or workplace; usually it will be developed by workers and cost accountants to reflect actual processes. A spreadsheet, kept at the workplace, may suffice

→ the teams have responsibility and authority to make small-scale changes

Kaizen costing is about beating the current cost levels, not matching standards and explaining variances.

PSEUDO PROFIT CENTRES

Pseudo Profit Centres take kaizen costing one step further. This is to make each workgroup a mini business. Instead of just costs, the team is given information on the "sales prices" of the items being manufactured. These prices may not be the actual company sales prices but may reflect internal transfer prices. (Once again, note similarities with OBM).

If operators are provided with the additional information to calculate "profits" (even though the profits may not be real), there are several strong advantages. Operators are able to prioritise improvement activities, which is really the essence of kaizen. They are also able to make decisions as which products to make if there is a shortage of time or capacity. Further, they are able to call in, or as it may happen not to call in, expert help from staff specialists such as industrial engineers or quality experts. The team may decide that expenditure on such expertise is just not warranted - an interesting turnabout from the usual situation of having consultants imposed upon them. And the team can begin to offer more informed advice on new investment. There may be bonuses associated with various levels of profit. All this is not to say that the team can do as they like. They still may have overriding goals to achieve such as meeting 100% delivery targets each week.

FURTHER READING:

Robert Kaplan and Robin Cooper, *Cost and Effect,* Harvard Business School Press, Boston, MA, 1998, ISBN 0-87584-788-9
Robin Cooper and Regine Slagmulder, *Kaizen Costing and Value Engineering,* Institute of Management Accountants / Productivity Press, Portland, OR, 1997 (Volume 3 of the series).

PERFORMANCE MEASUREMENT AND BALANCED SCORECARD

Kaplan and Johnson, in their famous book *Relevance Lost*, attacked corporate reporting systems saying that they were too oriented towards meeting the needs of the stockmarket, and that this was a major reason why Western manufacturing was losing out to Japan. For too long, performance measurement has been dominated by

➔ backward looking, and

➔ financial

measures of performance. It has been said that this is like a one-eyed person trying to drive a car by looking in the rear view mirror. Of course, what are needed are both financial and non-financial performance measures, looking forward as well as back.

Balanced Measures ?

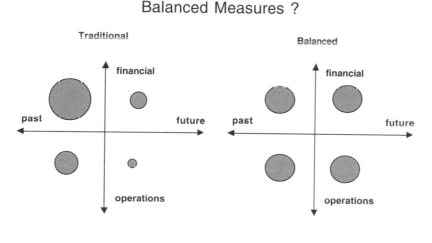

size of circle indicates number of measures

The "Balanced Scorecard", developed by Kaplan and Norton, is now widely recognised as being a significant advance in performance measurement. Kaplan and Norton's work puts forward a methodology for a balanced set of measures, whereby financial measures are but one element. According to them, there are four aspects that any performance measurement system needs to cover. These are Financial, Customer (or externally) oriented, Business Process (or internally) oriented, and "Learning and Growth". All are necessary. Moreover, there is logic that sees financial performance emerging form customer understanding, from internal operations, and these last two being sustained and renewed by learning and growth. See the figure.

Kaplan and Norton suggest that there are generic measures in each area. Some examples are :

Financial	Return on investment, return on assets employed, economic value added, profitability, revenue
Supplier	Cost, quality, delivery performance, kaizen activity
Customer	Satisfaction, acquisition, retention, market share
Internal process	Cost, quality, response time, productivity, inventory days
People	Employee satisfaction, employee turnover
Learning and Innovation.	New product introductions, improvements, suggestions.

The Balanced Scorecard

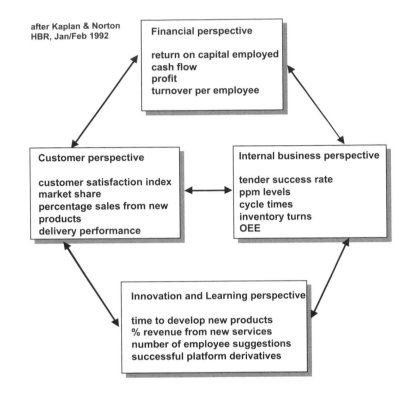

after Kaplan & Norton
HBR, Jan/Feb 1992

Financial perspective

return on capital employed
cash flow
profit
turnover per employee

Customer perspective

customer satisfaction index
market share
percentage sales from new
products
delivery performance

Internal business perspective

tender success rate
ppm levels
cycle times
inventory turns
OEE

Innovation and Learning perspective

time to develop new products
% revenue from new services
number of employee suggestions
successful platform derivatives

Moreover, Kaplan and Norton maintain that measures should be capable of "telling the story"; that is that they should form a logical sequence showing how learning and growth lead to operational growth, which are both assisted by customer or market orientation, which finally result in financial return for shareholders. Such a framework can be both top-down and bottom-up, with participation at all levels in much the same way as the Hoshin framework (see separate section).

These are the starting points for a performance measurement system. However, the Cambridge researchers believe that one should start with grouping products by family or strategic requirements (asking, for example, what makes a customer buy from you), before getting down to develop more detailed measures.

Andy Neely and Mike Bourne of Cambridge suggest a framework for checking out each measure, probably based on Kipling's Six Honest Serving Men:

The Measure:	a self-explanatory title
Purpose:	why is it being measured?
Relates to:	to which business objective does this measure relate?
Target:	what is to be achieved, and by when
Formula:	the formula or ratio used.
Frequency:	how often should the measure be taken, and reviewed
Who measures?	who is responsible for collection and reporting?
Source of data:	where does it come from
Who acts?	who is responsible for taking action?
What to do?	what action should be taken?
	and one could add
Limits:	what are the control limits within which no action is required?

Whilst the Balanced Scorecard is useful, many manufacturing and operations-based companies base their measurement systems on the central issues of the business which are Cost, Quality, Delivery, People, Suppliers, Markets, and New Product Introduction. The British DTI recommend seven measures: number of defects per million, units per operator hour, inventory turns, delivery achievement, OEE, value added per person, and turnover per floor area. Some examples of measures in each category follow. These may be presented in the form of a set of "Radar Charts" . This list can never be comprehensive, but gives an idea of currently used measures.

The important thing is to select a few appropriate measures from each category and then to look at them as a set, not individually. Also, try to measure by process rather than by function.

Cost

overtime hours

unscheduled stoppages (hours)

absenteeism

kaizen (number of activities)

OEE

products value engineered (%)

days of inventory (raw material, WIP, finished goods, distribution

lead time to work content ratio

die / tool change times (minutes)

value of inactive stock (£)

electricity used

Quality

ppm levels (at goods receiving, end of each stage, finished, distribution)

(note parts per million defects is far more effective than %)

complaints received

customer satisfaction / demerit score

audit (% operations to conformity) or audit score

capability (% machines with Cpk more than 1.5), achievement towards six sigma

cost of quality (£). (including all failures, rework, scrap, repair, warranty, emergency repair, etc.)

TPM (% of area covered, or operators trained)

customer turnover rate / retention rate

Delivery

Manufacturing lead time (hours)

Total lead-time, raw material to customer

Schedule linearity (i.e. deviation from level schedule)

ppm not delivered on time

delivery variability (the distribution from early to late)

inventory accuracy (% by class)

bill of material accuracy (%)

People. Safety, Morale

labour turnover

value added per operator and value added per person

lost time due to accidents

safety audit

investors in people

multi function workers (% fully functional)

training days per employee per year

kaizen participation rate or suggestions per month

Suppliers

number of "productive" suppliers, number "non-productive" suppliers

quality audits undertaken

number of certified suppliers

ppm delivered right first time, right on time

Markets

number of products contributing last 10% of contribution or profit

ratio of key accounts to non-key

New Product Introduction

new product introduction rate (profitable products per year)

time to market

time to break even

staff time per new product

new product introduction cost

number (or cost) of modifications, post manufacturing start

It will be seen that these measures can be fitted into the balanced scorecard.

Caplice and Sheffi suggest a useful framework for the evaluation of logistics measures. They suggest 8 criteria : (1) validity (measures what it is supposed to measure without distortion). (2) robustness (is comparable against time and repeatable), (3) integration (promotes co-ordination between functions, (4) level of detail (provides the appropriate level), (5) compatibility (with existing systems), (6) behavioural soundness (minimises the risks of individual 'game playing'), (7) usefulness (is easily understood by persons having to use it), (8) economy (the benefits of having the measure outweigh the costs of data collection and preparation).

A variation of the Balanced Scorecard, developed at Cambridge University, sees performance measurement in terms of an input/output model. Here there are six groups of necessary measures : suppliers, customers, internal processes, people, learning and innovation, and financial performance. See the figure.

WHAT TO MEASURE ?
6 Starting Points for Performance Measures

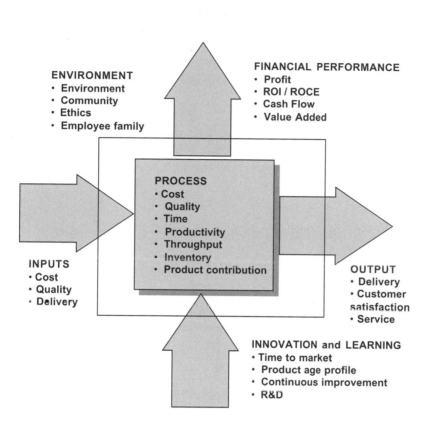

ENVIRONMENT
* Environment
* Community
* Ethics
* Employee family

FINANCIAL PERFORMANCE
* Profit
* ROI / ROCE
* Cash Flow
* Value Added

INPUTS
* Cost
* Quality
* Delivery

PROCESS
* Cost
* Quality
* Time
* Productivity
* Throughput
* Inventory
* Product contribution

OUTPUT
* Delivery
* Customer satisfaction
* Service

INNOVATION and LEARNING
* Time to market
* Product age profile
* Continuous improvement
* R&D

FURTHER READING:

Robert Kaplan and David Norton, *The Balanced Scorecard,* Harvard Business School Press, Boston, 1996. ISBN 0-87584-651-

Andy Neely, John Mills, Mike Gregory, Huw Richards, Ken Platts, Mike Bourne, *Getting a Measure of Your Business,* Works Management / University of Cambridge Manufacturing Engineering Group, 1996

D Caplice and Y Sheffi, "Review and Evaluation of Logistics Metrics", *Int Journal of Logistics Management,* Vol 5, No 2, 1994, pp 11-28

Richard Lynch and Kelvin *Cross, Measure Up,* Second ed., Blackwell, Oxford, 1995

DTI, *Quality Cost Delivery,* Dept of Trade and Industry, March 1998

PRODUCTIVITY ACCOUNTING

Like quality, productivity is a central concern of operations management. Although productivity can be defined in general terms as being the ratio of outputs to inputs, it is appropriate to begin looking at productivity by first looking at changes in profitability from one period to the next. (van Loggerenberg, 1988). An accountant would view a change in profitability from one period to the next as resulting from a change in revenues and/or a change in costs, as shown in the central column of the figure below. Here an increase in profit results from an increase in revenues or a decrease in cost, or some combination of the two.

Changes in revenue result from changes in product quantities and / or from changes in product prices. Likewise changes in costs result from changes in resource quantities (that is the numbers of people, machines, materials, and energy) and from changes in resource costs. This are shown in the top and bottom rows of the figure.

Profit, Productivity and Price Recovery

This completes the standard accounting view. Management accountants will seek to understand deviations from budgets by variances in each of these four areas. Operations managers are generally more interested in productivity change. Recall that a change in productivity results from changes in the ratio of product quantities to changes in resource quantities. This uses the familiar definition of productivity as being outputs / inputs. Likewise we can view a change in "price recovery" as resulting from a change in the ratio of product prices to changes in resource costs (or prices). Thus price over-recovery reflects a situation where prices of products are increased more than the costs of resources, and price under-recovery reflects the situation where the organisation absorbs some of the cost increases and does not increase the price of its products by as much as resource costs have risen.

Instead of seeking to explain changes in profit by the conventional accounting view of changes in revenue and changes in cost, a view more appropriate to the operations manager can be given. This is that changes in profit result from changes in productivity and from changes in price recovery.

We can explore this further with the help of productivity grids (van Loggerenberg, 1988). In the figure below, changes in productivity are shown on the vertical axis and changes in price recovery on the horizontal axis. No change takes place at the intersection of the two axes. A negative change in productivity is shown in the lower half of the figure; a negative change of course reflects a decline in the rate of productivity growth rather than an absolute decline in productivity. The same comments can be made about changes in price recovery with negative changes to the left of the vertical axis. Positive changes in profitability from one period to the next occur at any point above and to the right of the diagonal axis. Once again, a positive change means increased profit or decreased loss.

Is all Profit the same ?

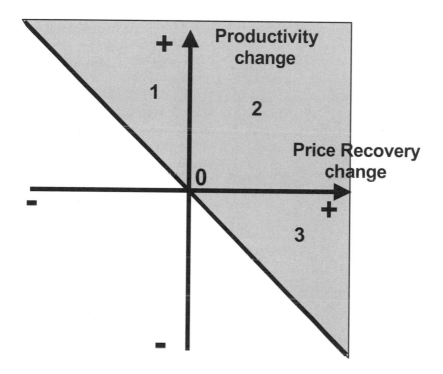

Profit change is positive above the diagonal.
A point plotted in the shaded area indicates a positive
change in profitability between two periods

Notice that there are three segments where positive changes to profit occur. In segment 2 both productivity change and price recovery change is positive. In segment 1 however, a negative change in price recovery is more than offset by a positive change in productivity. Clearly, this is a segment where competitive advantage is greatest. Prices are being, relatively speaking, cut whilst improved profits are being generated through productivity change. Remaining in this segment discourages competitors. The reverse is true in segment 3. Here increased profits are being generated through price increases that are offsetting a fall in productivity. Clearly, although increased profits are being made, this is the weakest position to be in. Remaining in this segment for too long represents an opportunity for competitors, particularly whose productivity is superior. Similar comments can be made about segments where a negative change in profit has occurred. So, an operations manager needs to know not just if increased profits are being made, but HOW those increased profits are being generated. To ignore this insight is folly.

FURTHER READING:
Bazil van Loggerenberg, *Productivity Accounting,* PICSIE Books, 1989

INDEX

5 S 113,126
ABC 190
Activity Based Costing 190
Agile 15-19
AME 117
Andon 112
Audits 105-107
Batch and Queue 13
Batch Sizing 144-146
Blitz 116
Bottleneck 73,145,164,127
BPR 132-134
Brown Paper 76
Buffer 139-140,165,159
Business Process Reengineering 98,132
CANDO 113
Cell 153
Changeover 140,144,148
Concurrent Engineering 45
Constraint 95
CONWIP 141
Cost 38,197,44
Cost Driver 190
Cost Time Profile 96
Customer 12,14,41-43,82,170
Cycle Time 83
Delivery 197
Demand 150
Demand Amplification 90
Demand Management 150
Dependent Event 163
Design 41-43
Design for Manufacture 50
Drum 164
Enforced Improvement 112
Failsafing 172
Flow 156
Ford 76
Gemba 28,186
Goldratt 163-169
Group Technology 153
Heijunka 151
Hines 78,181
Hoshin 34
Improvement 110
Innovation 44
Inventory 163,135,158
Jones 12-13,107
Juran 35

Kaikaku 115
Kaizen 28,124
Kaizen Costing 185,193
Kanban 136
Kano 170
Kobayashi 106
Layout 155
Lean Characteristics 14
Lean Principles 14-15
Lean Thinking 12-13
Level Schedule 151
Line Balancing 155
Mapping 78-96
Mass Customisation 48
Measurement 190-199
Mixed Model 149
Modularity 48
Muda 21-26,74
New Product Introduction 198
OEE 129
One Piece Flow 83
Open Book 184
Organisation 41
Overall Equipment Effectiveness 129
Pareto 73
Partnership 178
Passive Improvement 111
Perfection 13
Performance Measurement 195-198
Platforms 52
Pokayoke 172
POLCA 142
Precontrol 176
Press Shop 147
Prevention 174
Process 83,85,98
Production Flow Analysis 156
Productivity 200
Pull 12-13,93
QFD 57
Quality 90,170,197
Quality Circles 111
Repeaters 150
Root Cause 130
Rope 163
Runners 150
Scenario 30
Schonberger 107
Screening 65

SDWT 187-188

Self Directed Work Teams 187-188

Setup 129,144,148

Shingo 172,144

Short Run SPC 174

Simplicity 14-15

Simultaneous Engineering 45

Six Sigma.. 174

Soft Systems Methodology 102

SPC 174,176

Standards 118,186

Storyboarding 75

String Diagram 120

Supplier Partnership 178

Suppliers 94,178-181,198

Supply Chain 91,90,151

Synchronisation 164

System Dynamics 68,90

Systems Thinking 68,102

Takt Time 67,144

Target Costing 38

Thinking Process 166

Throughput 163

Time 41,100,44

Time Based Competition 19

Time Pacing 32

TOC 166-169

Total Productive Maintenance 126

Toyota 186,146

TPM 126

TRIZ 63

Ubuntu 188

Value 12-13,14-15,33,78,121

Value Stream... 78

Voice of the Customer 12-13

Waste 21-26,74